RECORDS RELATING TO

Personal Participation in World War II
AMERICAN PRISONERS OF WAR AND CIVILIAN INTERNEES

COMPILED BY

BENJAMIN L. DEWHITT & JENNIFER DAVIS HEAPS

REFERENCE INFORMATION PAPER 80

NATIONAL ARCHIVES AND RECORDS ADMINISTRATION
WASHINGTON, DC
REVISED 1998

United States. National Archives and Records Administration.
    Records Relating to Personal Participation in World War II: American prisoners of war and civilian internees/compiled by Ben DeWhitt and Jennifer Davis Heaps—Washington, DC: National Archives and Records Administration, 1999.
    vii, 84 p.; 23 cm.—(Reference information paper; 80rev)
    Includes index.

    1. United States. National Archives and Records Administration—Catalogs. 2. World War, 1939–1945—Personal narratives, American—Bibliography—Catalogs. 3.

42303476

COVER: *Roku Roshi POW Camp, Osaka, Japan.* Record Group 389, Records of the Office of the Provost Marshal General, 1941– , SC212143-S

For sale by the U.S. Government Printing Office
Superintendent of Documents, Mail Stop: SSPO, Washington, DC 20402-9328
ISBN 0-16-050200-4

Contents

Preface

This revised version of Reference Information Paper 80, *Records Relating to Personal Participation in World War II: American Prisoners of War and Civilian Internees,* is one of a publication series begun by the National Archives and Records Administration (NARA) more than 50 years ago. The format and style of papers like this one have varied over the years, but they generally consist of an introduction that places the topic in the context of Federal recordkeeping, followed by sections that describe and discuss specific pertinent records. The papers are part of a program that helps people inspect for themselves the record of what government has done and hold officials accountable for those actions.

NARA's descriptive program comprises a variety of information products. These include inventories, lists, guides, and reference information papers that, increasingly, are being made available to researchers in electronic as well as paper-based formats. Information products of particular interest to users of this reference information paper include: *Audiovisual Records in the National Archives of the United States Relating to World War II* (Reference Information Paper 70, 1992); *Records Relating to Personal Participation in World War II: "The American Soldier" Surveys* (Reference Information Paper 78, 1997 revised); *World War II Records in the Cartographic and Architectural Branch of the National Archives* (Reference Information Paper 79, 1992); *Records Relating to Personal Participation in World War II: American Military Casualties and Burials* (Reference Information Paper 82, 1993); *Records Relating to American Prisoners of War and Missing in Action from the Vietnam War Era, 1960–1994* (Reference Information Paper 90, 1995); *Records Relating to American Prisoners of War and Missing-in-Action Personnel from the Korean War and During the Cold War Era* (Reference Information Paper 102, 1997); *Guide to Records Relating to U.S. Military Participation in World War II, Part I: Policy, Planning, Administration* (1996) and *Part II Support and Supply* (1998); and *American Women and the U.S. Armed Forces: A Guide to the Records of Military Agencies in the National Archives Relating to American Women* (1992). A comprehensive source of information about the archival holdings of NARA is the *Guide to Federal Records in the National Archives of the United States* (1995). The text of that guide can be browsed electronically by accessing NARA's Web site at http://www.nara.gov. Other online resources available at this URL include the NARA Archival Information Locator, a pilot database of descriptions of selected holdings. The database includes, in particular, citations to many audiovisual resources relating to World War II.

NARA's mission is to ensure ready access to the essential evidence that documents the rights of American citizens, the actions of Federal officials, and the national experience. We hope that all of our information products will help citizens to more easily use the resources held in trust for them, and we welcome suggestions for ways to enhance our services.

John W. Carlin
ARCHIVIST OF THE UNITED STATES

Part I

I.1 This reference information paper covers records in the National Archives of the United States pertaining to both American military personnel who were captured by Axis forces and American civilians who were detained by the Axis powers during World War II. For the most part, "civilian internees" were included with Prisoners of War (POWs) in inquiries, diplomatic correspondence, War Department accounts, and even some postwar records. Their consideration was so intermixed with that of POWs that it is not advisable to treat them separately. The reverse is true in the records of the U.S. Department of State, wherein information on POWs is intermixed with that on civilian internees.

I.2 The search for information about a specific individual who was held by the enemy during the war requires, of course, knowledge of that individual's full name. In some cases that alone suffices, but any knowledge beyond a name can reduce search time and multiply resulting information to a remarkable degree. Useful supporting details include the person's service number, branch of service, unit, approximate dates of internment, and the Axis power by which he was detained. In many cases it is also helpful to know if the individual had a "prisoner number" or control number assigned by the detaining power. It might also be of value to know such details as what prison camp or camps the person was in, and when and where he or she was repatriated, interviewed, or "debriefed" by American or Allied authorities concerning his or her wartime experience. In a few cases even the names of foreign nationals who assisted the American in evading or escaping the enemy will be useful. In short, any scrap of information gleaned from personal memory, family records, published sources, or the like will reward the researcher with improved results from a search of Federal records.

I.3 The least one can expect from the records is verification of POW or civilian internee status. This is true in the vast majority of cases. Such verification at one location in the records can often provide added information such as hometown, next of kin, birth date, etc. This new knowledge combined with the other details mentioned above (such as the individual's military unit or camp name) can occasionally lead to texts of interviews with the subject, handwritten responses to Defense Department inquiries, or even photographs of the camp involved and, in rare cases, of the individual. While these finds are relatively rare, they can be rewarding.

I.4 A few of the records contain information of a personal nature that may be exempt from disclosure to researchers under provision B(6) of the Freedom of Information Act (FOIA). Examples of this are information about wounds or medical conditions, accounts of some incidents that occurred during captivity, and some photographs of individual prisoners. There are few of these kinds of records; and the application of FOIA exemptions must be decided on a case-by-case basis.

I.5 A very useful overview of prisoners of war in World War II may be found in "The ASF [Army Service Forces] in World War II: Volume II," [1945]–Chapter E, American Prisoners of War. This work is part of Record Group 160, Records of Headquarters Army Service Forces, among the records of the Office of the Commanding General, Control Division, Administrative Management Branch, in the series **historical file, 1941–46** (14 ft.). The overview was created for the use of the Commanding General, ASF, in preparing his report to the Chief of Staff. The section on American POWs, quoted below, provides an excellent summary of several processes and conditions that should be considered when seeking information in Federal records regarding individuals who were captives:

[1.] Responsibility has been delegated to the War Department to receive records on all American nationals in enemy custody. This included not only members of the Army but also the Navy, Marine Corps, Coast Guard, Merchant Marine and American civilians. The first United States nationals reported to be in Japanese custody were those civilians and Marine Corps garrison in the Shanghai area or its vicinity, followed closely by Naval personnel on Wake Island. Although the Japanese did sign the Geneva Convention, it was never officially ratified by them. However, it was intimated that they would adhere to its provisions. Reports received through the International Red Cross regarding American personnel captured by the Japanese were exceedingly slow and in many cases captures were not reported at all. This failure to promptly report American personnel in Japanese custody, together with the treatment accorded them by the Japanese, clearly indicates that Japan did not follow the Geneva Convention in any respect. The first reports concerning personnel captured in the Philippine Islands and adjacent territory were not received until December 1942.

[2.] In contrast to the slow, almost nonexistent, reporting system used by the Japanese government, the German government was reasonably prompt in reporting all prisoners of war up until the time when the over-running of German territory by the Allied Forces as well as the effects of air bombardment of German cities so disrupted the German administrative set-up that no more reports were made to Geneva. When an airman was shot down or a Ground Forces man was captured, reports of his fate came through from the German government within a month or 6 weeks, although at times it was 6 months before a report was received. This was partly due to the fact that the Germans did not report hospitalized wounded until they had been discharged from the hospital and were transferred to a prisoner of war camp. The German central Records Offices at Meiningen and Saalfeld were captured in April 1945 complete with all records and the operating personnel. These records were posted up to date and the ones which pertained to U.S. Army personnel were transferred to Washington, DC where they were invaluable in clearing up many cases of personnel who had died since the German government stopped reporting to Geneva.

[3.] A great deal of confusion occurred after the liberation of personnel in German prisoner of war camps because the prisoners of war did not 'stay put', but those liberated by the Allied Armies in the West started to hitch-hike to France, and those liberated by the Russian Armies in the East hitch-hiked toward Moscow. Obtaining rosters of names of liberated prisoners of war was further complicated because Air Forces personnel was [sic] flown out of Germany direct to England by the Eighth and Ninth Air Forces which made it difficult for the theater headquarters in Paris, France to obtain rosters of such personnel.

[4.] Repatriations under the Geneva Convention: No repatriations of the sick and wounded were arranged with the Japanese government since, as previously stated, Japan did not adhere to the Geneva Convention. Several repatriations were arranged with the German government. The first through Lisbon included 35 U.S. military personnel, the second through Barcelona included 65 U.S. military personnel, the third through Goteborg, Sweden included 250 U.S. military personnel, and the fourth through Marseilles, France consisted of 497 military personnel. In addition, a group of 75 protected personnel was repatriated.

[5.] At the end of hostilities with Germany 96,048 prisoners of war were carried as in the hands of Germany; 94,320 were accounted for as recovered alive; 1,368 were accounted for as having died, and 360 remain unaccounted for. Exhaustive efforts are now in progress to determine the fate of the latter men. At the cessation of hostilities with Japan 9,500 were carried as prisoners of war and 8,819 were carried as missing in action. Since the Japanese government, as stated before, very infrequently reported prisoners of war, it is expected that many of those listed as missing in action will be recovered alive from Japanese prisoner of war camps.

I.6   Thus the closing paragraphs of the introduction to the POW chapter of ASF's 1945 report foretell the continuing effort on the part of the Government of the United States to account for all of the American military personnel and civilians who fell into enemy hands during World War II. That effort was motivated by the military establishment's determination to account for its troops; by the insistence of the victorious Allied powers that war criminals be punished; by the Government's decision to inform its citizenry about the war; by the decision to pay reparations to individuals for their loss; and by the gratitude of the nation toward those who paid an extra, if not ultimate, price in their service to country. The records created by that effort are part of the documentation of the personal experience of those who were POWs or civilian internees.

I.7   Records regarding POWs and internees are divided into four categories for the purpose of discussion in this paper:

1. **Part II. Wartime POW Records**. Created in the process of collecting information about or keeping track of POWs and internees during or immediately after the war.

2. **Part III. Wartime Related Records**. Created during or immediately subsequent to the war in the process of gathering information, not about POWs but about specific classes of individuals or events to which POWs were in some way related.

3. **Part IV. Postwar POW Records**. Created well after the war to account for all POWs and civilian internees.

4. **Part V. Other Records.** Such as photographs, publicity material, and press releases.

Part II

Wartime POW Records

II.1 This section discusses records created by military agencies and the Department of State during and immediately subsequent to the war with the aim of collecting and organizing information about American POWs and civilian internees. The records of military agencies are described first, in general order from those series that are most productive of information on individuals to those that are least productive. State Department records are described last.

Record Group 389   Records of the Office of the Provost Marshal General, 1941–

II.2 During, and for a time after, World War II the Office of the Provost Marshal General (OPMG), an Army Special Staff agency and one of the major Army service organizations, was responsible for protective and law enforcement activities on an Army-wide basis. In many of its functions the office acted for both the Secretary of War and the Secretary of the Navy. Included in these duties was responsibility for prisoners of war, both American and American-held.

II.3 The central source for information about U.S. prisoners in enemy custody during World War II was OPMG's Prisoner of War Information Division (known as the Information Bureau of the Prisoner of War Division before December 1944). It collected, organized, and maintained information received from sources such as military intelligence organizations, the diplomatic community, the International Committee of the Red Cross, and the protecting powers. The division also handled the mail of prisoners of war. Much of the information concerned application of the Geneva Red Cross and Prisoner of War Conventions of 1929, identification of American military and civilian personnel in enemy custody, and facilitation of communications between American POWs and their families.

II.4 The ongoing mission of collecting and organizing information has made the records of the Prisoner of War Information Division an excellent source for historical and personal information about Americans who were prisoners of war during World War II. One good way to begin a search in this record group is to use a set of alphabetical name rosters of POWs and civilian internees. They consist of:

1. "POWs held by Germany" (24 vols.).

2. "POWs held by Japan" (6 vols.).

3. "POWs held in neutral countries" (1 vol.).

All volumes for POWs list name; serial number; last camp at which detained (with possible exceptions); fate of POW (such as KIA, killed in action, and RMC, returned to military control).

4. "American civilian internees held by Japan" (3 vols.).

In addition to listing civilian employees and their dependents who were interned, these volumes contain a section for Roman Catholic nuns held in the Philippines. Each Sister is listed and is cross-referenced to a listing under her civilian name.

5. "Miscellaneous lists of internees of other nationalities."

Some of these individuals were dependents of U.S. citizens and/or later became naturalized U.S. citizens.

Many of the entries in these alphabetical name rosters contain cross-references to cables or questionnaires that can be located in the general subject file of the POW Information Division (described immediately below).

THE POW INFORMATION BUREAU GENERAL SUBJECT FILE

II.5 The single most important group of records regarding the personal experiences of American prisoners of war during World War II is the series **general subject file, 1942–46** (64 ft.), consisting of correspondence, camp reports, diaries, rosters, and other records relating to Americans interned by Germany and Japan during the war. Also contained in this file are several indexes that identify individuals or direct the user to records that contain information on individuals. The most important of these "internal indexes" are identified and described in this paper. In the process of fulfilling its mission, the Information Division created, and to some extent automated, a series of separate indexes to the subject file. That series of indexes is described below under the heading "THE 'IBM CARDS'."

II.6 The subject file series is arranged alphabetically by subject titles that are a mixture of: (1) document types, such as "cables" and "messages"; (2) geographic locations, such as "Conarky, French Guinea" and "Java"; (3) content indicators, such as "casualty reports," "camp reports," and "interrogation reports"; and (4) others.

II.7 The irregularity of the subjects covered is best illustrated by the box list in Appendix A. Records can be reboxed relatively often in the processes of preservation and holdings maintenance; therefore this list is offered as a simple guide to the general contents of the records, not as a key to the exact locations of specific records. Certain subject classifications within the series contain records that are particularly rich in information about personal participation in World War II.

II.8 One such set of files for prisoners in the Pacific Theater is found under the heading "Camps–(followed by a geographic location indicator)." Most of these files contain letters, notes, diagrams, maps, photographs, and forms produced by American and a few Allied

POWs and by military personnel who were instrumental in liberating POW camps at the end of the war. The great bulk of the material consists of "first person accounts" or other information produced by former prisoners in response to the efforts of the American POW Information Bureau to produce a report on or a history of each camp where U.S. citizens were held.

II.9 Most of the accounts provided to the bureau are hand-written on a form that was sent to ex-POWs requesting their cooperation in documenting facts about the camps. Although some correspondents did not use the form but sent letters consisting of narrative descriptions instead, the information often covered the same subjects. A typical form, entitled "Check List," requested the following information:

1. Date of arrival at camp.
2. Location of camp.
3. When camp was first occupied and by what nationality.
4. Number of Americans interned and the name of the senior officer among them.
5. Personnel figures (American military personnel by branch of service, American civilians, and persons of other nationalities listed separately).
6. Identification of Japanese officers and other responsible individuals.
7. "Conditions," with subheadings for "Housing," "Latrines," "Bathing," "Mess," "Medical," and "Compound."
8. POW work.
9. Work conditions.
10. Mail.
11. Pay.
12. Red Cross Parcels.
13. Clothing.
14. Treatment.
15. Morale.
16. Religious facilities.
17. Date of departure.
18. Number of Americans departing.
19. Conditions en route.
20. Destinations.
21. A sketch of the compound.
22. Names of other individuals with information about the camp.
23. The name, rank, service number, organization, and home address of the respondent.
24. Any information considered relevant but not included in other categories.

Because these files constitute one of the richest sources of "first person" views of this aspect of the war in the Pacific, Appendix B is designed to provide access to the records by the locations and names of camps established by the Japanese.

II.10 Information about American POWs and internees who were in German or other enemy hands in the European Theater of Operations (ETO) during the war is generally more accessible than is information for those detained by the Japanese. Prisoner populations and camps were administered, and even named, in a more orderly manner in Europe. This can be seen fairly easily by looking at the box list in Appendix A (p. 42). Reasons for this probably lie in the broader and deeper European experience with prisoner populations during World War I and previous wars. In any case, this is the basis for the occasional focus on the Pacific Theater in this reference information paper.

The "IBM Cards"

II.11   The series of **IBM [punch] cards "subject index,"** n.d., was produced during World War II by the Prisoner of War Information Bureau, Office of the Provost Marshal General, United States Army, using Red Cross cables, other international messages concerning the status of POWs, and other records, most of which are in the POW Information Bureau subject file described in the previous section. (Researchers should be aware that, in spite of its title, this series is not truly a "subject index.") The carded information was maintained over the course of the war. Complete data are frequently not available for an individual. The National Archives has 11 files of cards (see **II.13**). The data elements in each of the files are identical, although the output from them varied somewhat in format. Most of the information punched into the cards is also printed at the top of each card. Name, serial number, rank, and camp at which detained are invariably printed. Two of the punch card files (the titles are preceded by an asterisk on the list) were used in the 1970s to produce a computer magnetic tape, a copy of which is also in the custody of NARA. The data elements in the files on that tape (see The Electronic Records, **II.14–16**) are typical of those in the 11 original punch card files.

II.12   The information on the punch cards, and thus on the computer tape, is far from consistent or complete. "Latest report date" and "camp location" are often missing. "Latest report date" sometimes refers to the date the file was closed and not the date the individual was released from POW status. "Camp location" sometimes refers to the camp in which the prisoner was first detained; sometimes it refers to the camp in which the prisoner was last detained. Indeed, since many prisoners were moved from camp to camp in both theaters of war, it very often falls short of revealing all locations at which a given individual was held. Also, some prisoners were assigned to constantly mobile details, and thus might have had no "camp location."

The Cards

II.13   The punch cards are arranged into files in the order given in the table below. Each file is arranged alphabetically by the surname of the individual for which there are records. The third entry contains information on prisoners who were aboard transport ships bound for camps in or near Japan when they were sunk. Each of these three files is arranged by the names of the transports and thereunder alphabetically by the surnames of the prisoners. The last file (Civilians) consists of two sets of cards, each arranged alphabetically by surname.

File Title / Notes	Approximate Size
1. American Civilian POWs (Released and Dead) Interned by Japanese	Boxes 1–10
2. Deceased American Prisoners (Japan)	Boxes 11–15
3. December, October, September Sinkings	Boxes 16–18
4. Neutral Internees	Boxes 19–20
*5. Released American POWs (Japan)[1]	Boxes 21–34
6. Deceased American POWs	Boxes 35–36
7. Killed in Action; Escapes; Never POWs (Germany)	Box 37
8. MIA-RMC	Boxes 38–39
*9. Released American POWs (Germany)[2]	Boxes 40–104
10. Civilians (A–Z)	Box 105

The Electronic Records

II.14   An electronic version of two of the punch card files was produced by the Veterans Administration (VA) in the late 1970s. It was used to assist in the VA's analysis of former POW "populations." It is important to remember that the electronic files cover only repatriated and only military POWs. The Pacific Theater data file contains 19,202 records. The European Theater data file contains 85,541 records. There are some records missing from the European Theater data file that are retained in the punch card file only:

1. The computer tape contains only 42 records with surnames that begin with letters from "W" through "Z." The punch card file (see above) contains 50 inches of cards with surnames from "W" through "Z." (There are approximately 120 cards in an inch.)

2. On the computer tape, there are only two records for surnames beginning with "Vo," and no records for surnames beginning with "V" alphabetized after the "Vo" entries. The card file contains 1.5 inches of cards (approximately 180) with surnames beginning with "Vo" and 0.25 inches of cards (approximately 30) with surnames beginning with "V" alphabetized after the "Vo" entries.

II.15   The data elements in the electonic files include:

1. Service Number
2. Name.

3. Rank.
4. Service Arm or Branch.
5. Date Reported.
6. Race.
7. State of Residence at Induction.
8. Type of Organization.
9. Parent Unit.
10. Area [of capture].
11. Latest Report [date].
12. Official [source of report].
13. Status.
14. Detaining Power.
15. Camp.
16. Repatriation status.

II.16   Information on these records is included in "Documentation for Data on Individual Repatriated U.S. Military Prisoners of War, World War II, European Theater and Pacific Theater," available from the Electronic and Special Media Records Services Division (NWME), National Archives and Records Administration, 8601 Adelphi Rd., College Park, MD 20740-6001.

Record Group 24   Records of the Bureau of Naval Personnel

II.17   The Bureau of Naval Personnel (BUPERS) was responsible for the full range of personnel functions for the U.S. Navy. The records of its Casualty Section for the World War II period pertain to Coast Guard personnel, Armed Guard units aboard merchant vessels, Navy aviation personnel, Navy nurses, and Women Accepted for Volunteer Emergency Service (WAVES); there is very little information regarding Marine Corps personnel.

II.18   Although the Army's Prisoner of War Information Division in the Provost Marshal General's Office (see Record Group 389, **II.2–II.4**) sought to account for all American POWs regardless of service, a researcher seeking more than basic information on an individual who served in the U.S. Navy should not stop with Army records. The Navy understandably sought to collect and keep information on its own personnel, and those records can confirm, and in many cases supplement, any information found in Army files.

II.19   BUPERS maintained information on Naval personnel through the work of the POW Board, a joint Army-Navy organization created in 1942 as part of its Casualty Section. **Navy Prisoner of War Board subject files, 1942–45** (9 ft.), are arranged according to an alphanumeric subject scheme. Since this subseries is central to the most complete set of records on Navy POWs in World War II in the National Archives, an annotated version of this file plan is produced in Appendix C. Related records are **general lists relating to prisoners of war** (2 ft.), consisting of naval and related personnel, arranged according to such factors as category of personnel, place of capture or incarceration, or time of liberation, and thereunder generally alphabetically by surname. There are, for instance, separate lists for Navy nurses and for civilian employees who were captured by the Japanese at specific installations in the Pacific. Another group of series, totaling approximately 7 feet, consists of general records, records about specific camps, and records about war crimes. These pertain to POWs in Japanese hands and are arranged informally by general subjects. The information in them supplements that which can be found in the subject files and lists described above.

Record Group 71   Records of the Bureau of Yards and Docks

II.20   The Bureau of Yards and Docks was responsible for the design, construction, and maintenance of all naval public works and utilities. Civilian construction workers employed by the Bureau at Wake Island were some of the first Americans taken prisoner by the Japanese when the war in the Pacific began. A similar fate soon befell workers in Guam, Shanghai, and the Philippines. As early as 1942 the U.S. Government began considering financial claims for which their dependents were eligible. The **administrative file, February–June 1942**, of the Bureau's Progress Division is reproduced on three rolls of 16 mm microfilm and contains extensive information on the claims.

II.21   The most significant personal information is found in "Report of Investigation of Dependency" compiled in 1942 by the Liberty Mutual Insurance Company under contract. It contains investigatory data on known dependents of construction workers killed or captured in December 1941. The data is arranged by location (vols. 1–6, Wake Island; vols. 6–7, Guam; vol. 7, Manila) and thereunder alphabetically by surname. There are also lists of the workers reported captured. The series also contains information on civilian construction workers lost on the SS *Lady Hawkins*, sunk by a German submarine in January 1942 en route to Bermuda, and on workers employed on Midway, Johnston, and Palmyra Islands, January-June 1942. Much of the investigative information is privileged.

Record Group 331   Records of Allied Operational and Occupation Headquarters, World War II

II.22   Great Britain and the United States controlled Allied efforts in World War II through the Combined Chiefs of Staff (CCS), established in January 1942. Supreme Headquarters Allied Expeditionary Forces (SHAEF) was set up under CCS in February 1944 as a combined British-American headquarters to direct military operations in Western Europe.

II.23   The **decimal correspondence file, 1944–45** (17 ft.), of the G-1 Division of SHAEF's General Staff contains, under decimal 383.6, "Prisoners of war," records concerning administrative and policy matters regarding location, relief, movement, and repatriation of American and Allied POWs in Europe, mostly during the time the war was drawing to a close. Some also concern Axis POWs and Americans and Allies who "escaped and evaded" the enemy. One set of maps (approximately 18 by 24 in.) are printed and titled "Location of PW Camps." The first is dated "1 Nov 1944"; the second is "Amended 1 Feb 1945"; and the third, "Amended 1 Mar 1945." Symbols on the printed map indicate the locations of camps of different classes and of hospitals and prisons. The amended maps have some symbols added by hand. In another series of the G-1 Division, **decimal correspondence**

file of the **Prisoner of War Executive Branch, 1944–45** (5 ft.), also in decimal 383.6, are some lists of Allied POWs, arranged by nationality.

II.24   Similar records, also under decimal 383.6, are found in **decimal correspondence file, May 1943–Aug. 1945** (36 ft.), in the records of SHAEF's Office of the Chief of Staff, Secretary, General Staff. There is an additional copy of the map "Location of PW Camps" that is "amended 26 Feb 1945." It has hand-drawn arrows that apparently indicate the proposed movement of repatriated POWs at the end of the war. There are also two lists:

1. "Location of Known and Possible Prisoner of War Installations in Germany and Occupied Countries as Known to PWX-G1-Division, SHAEF, at 18 March 1945," which has columns for camp serial number, location (latitude and longitude), "sheet number," "map referenced," type of camp, and notes.

2. "Location of P/W Camps in the British and U.S. Zones," 15 Aug 1944.

II.25   **Records of Allied Force Headquarters (AFHQ), 1942–46**, in box 85, microfilm reel R-33-M ("American P.O.W. Files," April–September 1945), contain lists of American POWs.

Record Group 242   National Archives Collection of Foreign Records Seized

II.26   Among the German records seized by United States forces during and after the war are [**carded records of American prisoners of war held by the Germans**] (25 ft.), consisting of forms maintained by the German Armed Forces High Command in an office analogous to the U.S. Army's Provost Marshal General. They are arranged alphabetically by the surnames of the POWs and contain information such as father's name, mother's name, date and place of birth, religion, service number, place and date of capture, general health, home address, and occupation. Some of the cards include a photograph of the individual.

Record Group 165   Records of the War Department General and Special Staffs

II.27   The series **interrogation reports and correspondence on Prisoners of War ("MIS-Y"), 1943–45** (125 ft.), is among the records of the Army Chief of Staff, G-2, Intelligence Division, Captured Personnel and Material Branch. These records were created primarily by interrogating Axis prisoners in American hands, so they contain very little easily accessible information on individual Americans. There are publications on conditions in POW camps in Germany, Japan, the Philippines, and Taiwan. A related series, **card index to correspondence in [the foregoing] series . . ., n.d.** (13 ft.), includes a set of 3- by 5-inch cards (8 in.) that index the few interviews conducted by the branch with escaped American POWs. The cards are arranged alphabetically by surname of POW and contain the following information:

1. Name.
2. Rank.
3. Service number.
4. Organization.
5. Escape date and route number.
6. Name of interviewer.
7. Dates of capture and return to military control.
8. Place of arrival in the United States.

Record Group 332   Records of U.S. Theaters of War, World War II

II.28   Records of the ETO, Provost Marshal Section, POW Information Bureau contain the following records that have information on American POWs in Europe:

1. "Lists of American Held in German-Controlled Territory, Mar–May 1945"; arranged by officer or enlisted status and thereunder alphabetically by name of POW or internee. Included are three supplementary lists and a list of codes used in the records.

2. "Card List of the Number of U.S. Personnel Held in POW Camps, 1944–45"; arranged alphabetically by country and thereunder numerically by type of facility.

3. "Reports of POW Camps, 1944–45"; arranged by country and thereunder by camp.

4. "Roster of Personnel Missing in Action, 1945"; arranged by officer or enlisted status and thereunder by serial number.

5. "Special Wanted Lists; Personnel Missing in MTOUSA: Correspondend re German POW Camps"; contains strength reports of POW camps in Germany, a roster of MIAs arranged by officer or enlisted status, changes in lists of unrecovered POWs, and a list of U.S. personnel interned in neutral countries.

6. "Nominal Rolls of American Held as Prisoners of War, 1945" (12 boxes); arranged alphabetically or numerically by name or number of POW camp or American medical installation, base section, military unit, or miscellaneous facility where Americans were liberated or released.

7. "Annotated Printouts of Nominal Prisoner of War Rolls, 1945"; arranged by nominal rolls and thereunder by status—returned to military control in battle casualty status, non-battle casualty status, or hospitalization not required—and thereunder alphabetically by name.

8. "Certificates of POWs, 1945"; signed by returned POWs acknowledging duty to prevent disclosure of military information and arranged numerically by registration number and thereunder alphabetically by name.

II.29   The Department of State's Special Division was created in September 1939 to deal with the growing number of diplomatic problems arising from the outbreak of war in Europe. It was renamed the Special War Problems Division in 1943. The division's records deal as much with Axis POWs and citizens "caught by war" in the United States and American-held territory as with American POWs and civilian internees in enemy hands. They contain far more information about civilian internees than about POWs. The records also contain much information about property settlements related to the war. They extend far beyond the war years into the 1950s, dealing with war-generated problems such as refugees and "displaced persons," especially concerning their relocation to the United States.

II.30   The series **policy books, 1939–45**, consists mostly of records dealing with administrative and policy details concerning both American and Axis POWs; but "Vol. 27, POW Representation," contains a copy of volume 2 number 1 of *Prisoners of War Bulletin*, published by the American National Red Cross. The bulletin was begun in June 1943 to keep the families of American POWs informed. It included advice on what kinds of exchanges of parcels and communications were allowed with prisoners under the Geneva Conventions. The publication contains excerpts of POW letters, pictures of POWs, and answers to questions from the families of POWs. A complete run of this publication may be found in the records of the Bureau of Naval Personnel (see Appendix C).

II.31   Another series, **inspection reports on war relocation centers, 1942–46**, deals mostly with stateside installations, but contains five folders on "Americans in the Philippines." There is a list titled "Americans in the Philippines, July–September 1942" that contains only names. The folder "Americans in the Philippines, June–December 1943" contains correspondence and narrative descriptions of conditions in POW camps, but no lists of names. "Americans in the Philippines, 1945," consists of 134 pages of lists of internees. All of the 12 lists are arranged alphabetically by the surnames of the internees and reveal their sex, age, nationality of birth, and marital status. Some lists contain addresses of internees. The lists are:

1. "Santo Tomas Camp, May 1943"—8 lists, broken down by categories such as "Protestant clergy" and "Roman Catholic clergy."
2. "Outside of Santo Tomas Camp in Manila."
3. "Los Banos."
4. "Camp Holmes."
5. "Davao."

II.32   The most useful series in the records of the Special War Problems Division is **subject files, 1939–54**. It is arranged by an extensive but vague subject scheme. Access is greatly facilitated by a box list created by NARA, much of which consists of folder titles. The records about property settlements, Axis POWs and citizens, and American POWs and civilian internees are so intermixed that the researcher should take time to read this extensive box list with his or her own interests in mind. The following are examples of the most obviously important records concerning Americans:

1. In boxes 65–69 there are lists (20 in.) of passengers who sailed on the vessels that repatriated citizens of both sides during and after the war. Most of those listed were aboard the Drottningholm or the Gripsholm, which traveled to and from several ports, among them Gothenburg, Lisbon, New York, and various locations in South America. The records are arranged chronologically by voyage. Most of the lists are arranged alphabetically by passengers' surnames and reveal their name, sex, nationality, age, and marital status. Some lists include the passengers' home addresses.

2. Boxes 70–71 contain various lists, including:

   a. "Americans at Baden-Baden" (1 in.), in the form of cards containing only names and occupations.
   b. Several lists (4 in.) of internees who sailed to the United States aboard U.S. Army transports in early 1942, arranged chronologically by voyage.
   c. "March 27, 1943 list of internees in the Philippines" (36 pp.), arranged alphabetically by surname with next of kin's address and relationship provided.
   d. A list supplemental to the one immediately above (10 pp.) dated April 17, 1943.

3. There is correspondence (8 in.) in boxes 89–92 concerning the treatment of Americans in POW camps. The records are arranged by camp name and number, with Japanese camps followed by German camps. Within each camp file the correspondence is arranged chronologically. Individuals' names are scattered throughout the records.

4. A "List of American Internees in the Far East (August 27, 1945)" (approximately 150 pp.) is in box 123. It includes 2,000 to 3,000 names arranged by 16 locations covering the entire Japanese camp system. For each location or camp, the names are arranged in approximate alphabetical order. Information for each name includes:

   a. Name and date of birth (the latter is often missing).
   b. Place of internment or residence (sometimes only the name of a city is given).
   c. Special notes (sometimes includes occupation and employer, confirmation of citizenship, or circumstances of capture).

In the same box is a list of internees aboard the SS *Admiral William L. Capps*, which arrived at San Francisco on April 8, 1945. It is arranged alphabetically by surname and includes name, age, employer, and next of kin.

5. More repatriations by means of ships crossing the Pacific after mid-1945 are accounted for in lists (3 in.) found in box 127. They are arranged by voyage and thereunder generally alphabetically by passengers' names. Information given includes name, age, employer, and next of kin. A few voyages of repatriation from Europe are in this box. It also contains lists of Americans in German camps, arranged by camp and including name, date of birth, and next of kin. Box 128 and boxes 130–135 (30 in.) contain similar lists arranged by camp location and repatriation ship voyage. They are in no discernible order, but the box list for the series includes each file name.

II.33 Department of State records other than those of the Special War Problems Division contain records relevant to the wartime experiences of American POWs and civilian internees. They are invariably less concentrated and less accessible, but may be used to great advantage in conjunction with the records of the Special Division and the Special War Problems Division. The most important of these is the State Department Decimal File, which includes substantial segments on the topic in decimals such as

711.62114	U.S. Prisoners of Germany
711.94114	U.S. Prisoners of Japan
740.00114a	U.S. POWs—European War
740.00115	Civilian Prisoners—European War

These records can be accessed through the decimal file's name index, its source index, and the "purport" list and cards.

Part III

Wartime Related Records

III.1   The records described in this section were created and collected during and immediately subsequent to the war for reasons other than accounting for or identifying American POWs or civilian internees. They were, however, aimed at documenting specific classes of individuals or events that bore some relationship to POWs and, in a few cases,
internees. Therefore, information on prisoners is less easily accessible in these records
than in those described above; and it is more likely to be found if the researcher already
knows something about the experience of the individual in question, such as important
dates, camp names, or the location of an air crash. The descriptions are arranged into five
general subject categories and, with the exception of war crimes records, are thereunder
presented in order by record group number. The war crimes records are arranged by
record group, but roughly in the order in which they were created—that is, records collected during the war precede those assembled upon the occupation of Japan, which in
turn precede the records created by the war crimes trials of the late 1940s.

RECORDS OF WAR CRIMES

III.2   Records that relate to war crimes during World War II, or allegations thereof, often
contain information about POWs because much of the conduct covered by the Geneva
Conventions pertained to the treatment of military or civilian prisoners of belligerent
nations. Many records were maintained throughout the war to account for personnel; to
inform stateside families and friends of the status of individuals; to furnish information on
which to base proposed exchanges of POWs; and at times to provide evidence for propaganda that the enemy was mistreating Americans. Immediately subsequent to the war, systematic efforts were made to investigate and document alleged war crimes with the aim of
trying those citizens of the defeated Axis powers held to be responsible for the transgres-
sions. This, of course, produced a wealth of record material.

Record Group 153   Records of the Office of the Judge Advocate General (Army)

III.3   During the war the Judge Advocate General's Department assumed responsibility
for the preparation of war crimes cases against Axis leaders. It fulfilled the staff function
for the War Department's share of U.S. participation in the United Nations War Crimes
Commission. After the appointment in May 1945 of Justice Robert H. Jackson as U.S. Chief
Counsel for the Prosecution of Axis Criminality, the War Crimes Office concentrated on
preparing charges against the lesser alleged war criminals, although it also aided the Chief
Counsel's staff in preparing cases against the major defendants.

**III.4 Reports of interviews with American servicemen who were prisoners of war,
1943–47** (75 ft.), were created and used by the Judge Advocate General's staff in investigating possible war crimes in both the European and the Pacific Theaters. Although there are index cards to this series, it is best to use them sparingly, because they cover only part of the records. The cards are an index by incident or category of incident and list only a few interviews or depositions that are representative of the subject. The series consists of 180 boxes of records arranged in 7 sections. Most of them are either depositions (averaging about 5 pages each) or single-sheet questionnaires. The depositions are much more useful concerning personal experiences during the war, because they focus on a single incident or condition in a specific POW camp or among a specific group of POWs. They also often contain narrative descriptions of events or conditions. The single-sheet questionnaires simply seek to determine if the respondent knows of any possible war crimes.

III.5 The name of a former POW is the key to finding information in this series. Because the records are arranged, at the first level, according to the date on which the former POW was interviewed, it is also helpful to know when the individual was interviewed concerning war crimes. Folders in the seven sections of the series are labeled as follows:

1. "1943-46. Alphabetically Arranged. Letter [ ]." Boxes 1–104. These depositions are arranged alphabetically by the surname of the interviewee and labeled according to the first letter of the surnames.

2. "1945. Alphabetically Arranged. Letter [ ]." Boxes 105–117. These are single-sheet questionnaires arranged in the same manner as the foregoing depositions.

3. "1945. Alphabetically Arranged. Miscellaneous." Boxes 117–118. These are mostly questionnaires, with a few depositions. They are only loosely arranged alphabetically by surname.

4. "1943-46. Unarranged." Boxes 118-138. These are questionnaires.

5. "1943-46. Interviews with Repatriates and Nurse Questionnaires." Box 138. The "interviews," which are unarranged, are lists of repatriated former POWs who were interviewed. The nurses' questionnaires, also unarranged, contain very little information about incidents or conditions.

6. "[Month] 1945: Letters [ ]. (Chronologically Arranged)." Boxes 139–175. These are mostly depositions. They are arranged by month of interview (May through November) and thereunder roughly alphabetically by surname of interviewee. "Letters [ ]" refers to the folder titles, each of which generally contains interviews of subjects with surnames beginning with a range of letters (such as "K–L–M").

7. "(Miscellaneous) May-November 1945, Letter [ ]." Boxes 175-180. These are depositions that are arranged alphabetically by surname as in the foregoing file.

III.6 Also part of the records of the Judge Advocate General's Department are **case files,
1944–49**, which are arranged into files about a specific war crime or group of related war

crimes. The records in the files are varied, including correspondence, trial records and transcripts, investigatory material, petitions, photographs, and published material. Some of the records, such as depositions of former POWs, contain information on conditions in specific locations and on the experiences of identified individuals. There is an extensive set of indexes for the case files, including ones arranged by the locations of incidents and the names of persons involved.

Record Group 331   Records of Allied Operational and Occupation Headquarters, World War II

III.7   General Headquarters, Supreme Commander for the Allied Powers (SCAP), was organized in October 1945 to carry out the occupation of Japan and the terms of the Japanese surrender. SCAP records include much material on war crimes investigations and trials. The records of the Legal Section (approximately 1,260 ft.) contain investigative and case files that generally focus on specific allegations of war crimes or on specific Japanese individuals accused of such activities.

III.8   One series in the Administrative Division of the Legal Section, however, was collected specifically to provide information about U.S. citizens who were prisoners of the Japanese. This is the **prisoner of war ("201") file** (20 ft.).[3] It permits easy access to records about the experiences of individuals, since it is arranged alphabetically by the surnames of former POWs. Each file contains copies of depositions concerning incidents or conditions in which the specific individual played a role. Thus, the file for "Doe, John," would contain Doe's deposition, but would also have copies of those of Richard Roe and John Q. Public whose wartime experience related in some way to Doe's. And Roe and Public would have their own files, each of which usually would contain the depositions of the other two former POWs.

III.9   The records of the Administrative Division also include series based on the names or nicknames of alleged war criminals among the Japanese, such as **P-201 perpetrators and suspected war criminals** (13 ft.), **prisoner of war "201" file** (65 ft.), and **suspected Japanese war criminals** (6 ft.). These series are accessible through a card index of Japanese names, or through the identification of Japanese names mentioned in those series that are keyed to POW names. That is, there are cases, in several series of records, in which identifiable American POWs reveal the names of their Japanese captors, or the nicknames they gave to them. Some of those Japanese names and nicknames maybe found in this file. However, for the purpose of determining the experiences of individual Americans these series are definitely secondary to the **prisoner of war file** described in the preceding paragraph. (See Record Group 319, **III.28**, for a description of related records.)

Record Group 238   National Archives Collection of World War II War Crimes Records

III.10   The most extensive collection of National Archives records on war crimes is a result of the Allied Powers' efforts, in the immediate aftermath of the war, to pursue and punish several Axis leaders and organizations for their participation in war crimes. Because of the scope of this effort, and because of the lack of precedents in dealing with atrocities of the magnitude committed during World War II, three tribunals were established. Record Group 238 is organized into subgroups of the records of U.S. participation in those three bodies:

1. International Military Tribunal (IMT);
2. U.S. Military Tribunals, Nuernberg; and
3. International Military Tribunal for the Far East (IMTFE).

Records of the International Military Tribunal (IMT)

III.11   In August 1945 the United States signed an agreement with representatives of the French, British, and Soviet Governments establishing an International Military Tribunal (IMT) to try war criminals. All those tried by IMT were German individuals or organizations accused of committing crimes in continental Europe. To facilitate the proceedings of IMT, the Office of the Chief of Counsel was formed. Its operation consisted of interrogation, documentation, and special projects units, and four committees, each of which specialized in compiling evidence that related to a corresponding category of war crimes.

III.12   Records pertinent to POWs are found in several series in the records of IMT. Court testimony, evidence and exhibits used at the trial, as well as information gathered in several files maintained by the Office of the U.S. Chief of Counsel for the Prosecution of Axis Criminality all provide perspectives on the experiences of those individuals who were POWs during World War II.

1. **Transcripts of proceedings of the tribunal, Nov. 20, 1945–Oct. 1, 1946** (20 ft.), are chronologically arranged IMT transcripts. Much of the information found here relates to group experiences during the war. POW camps, living conditions in these camps, forced POW slave labor, and the lynchings and murders of American military personnel are described. A portion of the testimony is given by former American POWs; and other witnesses give detailed accounts of the events surrounding the deaths of servicemen. Included is specific information about the victims, such as name, rank, branch of service, and unit.

2. **United States evidence files, 1945–46** (144 ft.), are comprised of documents collected by the Office of the Chief of Counsel and by the British to be used as evidence at the trial. This includes Staff Evidence Analysis Forms (SEA's), which are comprehensive English translations of German documents, or excerpts thereof, seized by the Allied Powers. Some refer to specific decrees, policies, and camps. This series contains more than 150 entry registers for a number of German concentration camps. For instance, entries for American POWs are located among "Buchenwald" register entry numbers. In addition to names of prisoners, the entries provide the date of admittance to the camp and, where applicable, the date of transfer or release. Although there are no name indexes to these registers, POW information similar to that available for Buchenwald

may be found in other camp entry registers. Almost all entry registers are arranged chronologically, by date of the prisoners' entry into the camp.

3. **United States exhibits, Nos. 1–930, 1933–46** (26 ft.), are the evidence file documents that were submitted to the court and became exhibits of IMT, arranged by assigned exhibit number. These records provide information on the illegal use of American POWs, their placement in concentration camps, and their use as slave laborers, as well as information on the formulation of German policies with regard to the murder and lynching of Americans, including official interpretations of German civilian attitudes towards such servicemen.

4. **Reference files, 1933–46** (36 ft.), used by IMT contain copies of two reports generated by the Office of the Provost Marshal General:

"American Civilian Internees Formerly Detained By the Japanese Government (including War, Navy and Merchant Marine Personnel), 7 December 1941–14 August 1945," and

"American Civilian Internees Formerly Detained By the German Government (including War, Navy and Merchant Marine Personnel), 11 December 1941–8 May 1945."

They list thousands of internees alphabetically by surname, along with the "arm of service" of the individual, his or her race, the date the internment was reported, the detaining power, concentration camp number (if applicable), and the official status of the case. Although some of the information is numerically coded, keys to the coding system are filed within the records. Also included in this series are approximately 75 photographic negatives (35 mm) of U.S. servicemen interned at Krems, Austria, that depict their living conditions. There are pictures of individual (unidentified) soldiers, their living quarters, clothing, and everyday activities during internment.

5. **Security-classified miscellaneous records, 1945–46**, contain various "Reports of the Supreme Headquarters, Allied Expeditionary Force," regarding the shooting of American prisoners of war by the German armed forces. These reports include testimony of witnesses giving explicit details of the circumstances surrounding the deaths; victim's name, rank, serial number, and unit; pathology reports; photographs and maps of the scene of the incident; diagrams; official correspondence regarding inquiries; and inquiry findings.

6. **Security-classified general correspondence [of the Washington Branch Office of the Office of the U.S. Chief of Counsel for the Prosecution of Axis Criminality], 1945–46** (6 ft.), contains further information on such war crimes committed not only against American military personnel, but against American civilians. The records are arranged according to the War Department decimal classification scheme, with some unarranged records at the end of the series. In folders labeled "Main Office Files" are individual case summaries. Each summary furnishes the names of persons involved and

gives a description of the relevant incident. References are also made to the beating and torture of American nationals.

RECORDS OF THE U.S. MILITARY TRIBUNALS, NUERNBERG

III.13   Subsequent to the IMT there were 12 war crimes trials held in Nuernberg, Germany, between October 1946 and April 1949. Under the authority of Allied Control Council Law No. 10, the military governor of the U.S. Zone of Occupation, General Joseph T. McNarney, established military tribunals to hear war crimes cases. These trials are collectively known as the U.S. Military Tribunals, Nuernberg, or the "Subsequent Proceedings." The records associated with these proceedings constitute a second subgroup of RG 238. The National Archives publication **Preliminary Inventory of the Textual Records of the United States Military Tribunals, Nuernberg** (1966) gives a useful overview of the records in this subgroup.

III.14   While general information on POW experiences may be found throughout the testimony and other records of the tribunals, the most accessible source regarding treatment of American prisoners is English transcripts of the proceedings [of *United States* v. *Wilhelm von Leeb, et al.* (High Command Case)], Dec. 30, 1947–Oct. 29, 1948 (24 vols., 5 ft.), arranged chronologically. Included in this series is testimony from surviving American POWs. Testimony in the case identifies American POWs as victims of "murder and ill treatment," mainly under Adolf Hitler's "Commando Order" and "Terror Flyer" order. While the other 11 cases tried at Nuernberg partially concern treatment of POWs, all of them deal with Russian and other Allied prisoners. Only the "High Command" case specifically addresses the experiences of American POWs. The most easily accessible source of information about this and related cases is the National Archives microfilm publication **Records of the United States Nuernberg War Crimes Trials, *United States of America* v. *Wilhelm von Leeb et al.* (Case XII) November 28, 1947–October 28, 1948** (M898). The microfilm contains the English transcripts described above, as well as related records. A descriptive pamphlet accompanying the microfilm (and available separately) provides general information on the Nuernberg trials and records related to them. See also **V.21**.

RECORDS OF THE INTERNATIONAL MILITARY TRIBUNAL FOR THE FAR EAST (IMTFE)

III.15   This tribunal was established by a special proclamation issued in January 1946 by General Douglas MacArthur, Supreme Commander for the Allied Powers (SCAP). As at Nuernberg, major offenders were to be prosecuted by an international agency before an international court. IMTFE was empowered "to try and punish Far Eastern war criminals who as individuals or as members of organizations are charged with offenses . . . ."

III.16   IMTFE records differ from those in the other two subgroups of Record Group 238 in that a far greater portion of the testimony, affidavits, and statements submitted into evidence are from American, as opposed to Allied, nationals. **The Tokyo Trials: A Functional**

Index to the Proceedings of the International Military Tribunal for the Far East (Ann Arbor: 1957), compiled by Paul S. Dull and Michael Takaaki Umemura, contains a comprehensive subject and name index that facilitates use of the records. Another valuable finding aid is the National Archives publication **Preliminary Inventory of the Records of the International Military Tribunal for the Far East** (PI 180, 1975). Searches can also be refined in many cases by using the indexes and lists among the records themselves, which are herein described with their related series.

III.17   Court exhibits, 1946–48 (85 ft.), are arranged numerically and consist of a wide variety of published and unpublished documents mainly from American and Japanese sources. Most of the Japanese items are accompanied by English translations. The exhibits include lists of POWs punished by Japanese Army courts martial, personal letters and diaries of American nationals, eyewitness accounts of Japanese war atrocities, and government reports from boards of inquiry pertaining to certain of the major atrocities committed by the Japanese. **List of court exhibits, 1948** (9 vols., 5 in.), is an accompanying finding aid arranged by exhibit number. Each entry contains information on the exhibit itself and the number of the page in the court proceedings on which the document is offered in evidence.

III.18   Transcript of the proceedings, Apr. 29, 1946–Nov. 12, 1948 (31 ft.), consists of 74 volumes arranged chronologically. Daily tables of contents precede each day's transcript, which is a verbatim account of the proceedings of IMTFE sitting in open court. The texts of some exhibits are included. This series contains information about general conditions in the POW camps, policies and regulations regarding captured American officers, civilian internee experiences, and summaries of major wartime episodes such as the Bataan Death March. Three indexes among the records, prepared by the International Prosecution Section of SCAP, are very helpful in using the transcripts. Two are arranged alphabetically by name and subject, with additional entries under the main headings also arranged alphabetically. They are:

1. **name and subject index to part (pp. 1–16977) of [transcript of the proceedings . . .], June 30, 1947** (1 vol., .5 in.), and

2. **name and subject index to part (pp. 16978–24758) of [transcript of the proceedings . . .], Oct. 10, 1947** (1 vol., 1 in.).

Another index to the same series is itself arranged into two subseries, one each for prosecution and defense witnesses, who are listed alphabetically by surname. It is **name indexes of witnesses [in transcript of proceedings . . .]**, n.d. (1 vol., 1 in.).

THE PHILIPPINE ARCHIVES COLLECTION

Record Group 407   Records of the Adjutant General's Office, 1917–

III.19   The Philippine Archives Collection is a subgroup of Record Group 407, Records of the Adjutant General's Office, 1917– . The records were created, compiled, and collected by the Army's Recovered Personnel Division (RPD), which initially was responsible only for processing recovered POWs and civilian internees, but later processed back pay and benefits claims as well as determinations of the loyalty status of Filipinos. Thus the files are a good source of information concerning the treatment and experiences of American POWs and civilian internees, military operations, and guerrilla warfare in the Philippines during the war. It is very important, however, to realize that factors such as the nature of guerrilla operations and the loss of records have the effect of limiting the accuracy, comprehensiveness, and completeness of the information conveyed in these records.

III.20 There are approximately 700 ft. of paper records and 120 rolls of microfilm in the Philippine Archives Collection. The records have been removed from their original numeric filing scheme and are now arranged in general subject categories (e.g., "Invasion and Surrender," "Guerrillas"), with subcategories (e.g., "Wartime Activities Other than Bataan and Corregidor"), or in categories by types of records (e.g., "Civilian Internee Death Report Files"). Material on many subjects is intermingled. Many of the records are in poor physical condition because of wartime circumstances. For instance, the scarcity of writing paper led to the use of scraps, tissue, labels, paper bags, and other odd materials; and the necessity for secrecy forced some persons to bury records for months or years and retrieve them at war's end. Because of these limitations, it is advisable to use this collection in conjunction with other more complete and better-arranged records on American personnel in World War II.

III.21 Portions of approximately 21 series of textual records in the collection have been microfilmed onto numbered rolls. A significant number of records in this form are illegible. Finding aids to the microfilm include roll-by-roll listings of contents and an alphabetical subject index.

III.22 Several series in the collection contain details of the experiences of American POWs and civilian internees:

1. **POW general correspondence files, 1941–45** (7 ft. and microfilm), include information on POWs and civilian internees in Japan and other parts of Asia, as well as in the Philippines; arranged by name of camp.

2. **POW recovery team report files, 1944–45** (2 ft.), are unarranged, but document such subjects as food, clothing, sanitary and health conditions, discipline, pay, and routine administration in the camps.

3. **Rosters and lists of POWs, 1942–47** (27 ft. and microfilm), and **POW death reports, 1941-46** (10 ft. and microfilm), are both arranged by camp name and thereunder either alphabetically by POW surname or chronologically. Some camp lists are arranged by nationality and thereunder alphabetically by surname.

4. **Diaries and historical narratives, 1940–45** (10 ft. and microfilm rolls AGRP 88, 89, 99, 105, and 110), are significant for their personal accounts of the war, captivity, and liberation. They are arranged alphabetically by the surname of the POW or civilian internee. The great majority of them are photocopies, not originals.

5. **Medical records of POWs and civilian internees, 1942–45** (11 ft. and microfilm), provide information on general conditions and on tropical diseases, as well as individual medical data. They are arranged by camp and thereunder generally alphabetically by surname.

6. **Sunken POW transport files, 1942, 1944–48** (2 ft. and microfilm), contain information (including names) about American POWs lost in the sinking of Japanese vessels during the war. They are arranged by the names of the ships.

7. **Records of Japanese atrocities against POWs, 1942–45, 1948** (1 ft. and microfilm), and **POW photographs, 1944-45**, both contain information on individuals, but are unarranged. It is difficult to locate and identify specific individuals in them.

8. **General correspondence files pertaining to civilian internees, 1943–45** (2 ft. and microfilm), are arranged by internment camp.

9. **Civilian internee rosters, 1942–46** (16 ft.), are arranged into two subseries. The first is arranged alphabetically by surname of internee, as indicated on Japanese identification cards. The second subseries is arranged by camp and thereunder alphabetically by internee surname.

10. **Civilian internee death report files, 1941–45**, is a small series and is unarranged, but includes information about civilians who died at the Los Banos and Santo Tomas camps, and about civilian employees of the U.S. Navy who were captured at Wake Island and died while in Japanese custody.

11. **Prison camp location files, 1945** (less than 1 ft.), unarranged, have information on the locations and general characteristics of various POW camps.

12. **Recovery and repatriation procedures and reports files, 1941–46, 1950–53** (1 ft.), unarranged, contain details of RPD activities in repatriating POWs. There are accounts of the deaths of POWs in Camp O'Donnell, Luzon, and conditions in the Nagasaki camp a month after the atomic bomb was dropped on that city.

RECORDS OF MISSING AIR CREWS (MACRs)

Record Group 92 Records of the Office of the Quartermaster General

III.23 One of the vital functions of the Quartermaster Corps in wartime is to account for and see to the proper disposition of the remains of deceased members of the armed forces. This includes notification of next of kin and proper memorialization of the dead. The series **reports of missing air crews, 1943–47** (118 ft.), arranged numerically in case files, was used initially for the purpose of notifying next of kin of the status of missing air crew members. The dates in the series title, 1943–47, refer to the time span of the investigations, not the air crew losses themselves; the series covers only wartime losses. After the war the MACRs were transferred to the Identification Branch of the Memorial Division, Office of the Quartermaster General. Some of the personnel in missing air crews are identified as captured by the enemy or as having died in enemy hands. The MACRs should never be consulted alone, without attempting to find other records to account for an American POW, but they might contain information that supplements or confirms information in files related more directly to POWs. In a very few cases the MACRs may be the only documentation available concerning a given individual.

III.24 More complete information about MACRs may also be found in the NARA publication *Records Relating to Personal Participation in World War II: American Military Casualties and Burials* (RIP 82). It contains a more thorough description of the records than is found in paragraph **III.23**, including a history of the records system, a description of the indexes to the MACRs, an outline of the information contained in a " typical" MACR, and cross-references to related records in other record groups.

III.25 The **lists of allied air crashes, Sept. 1939–Mar. 1945** (4 in.), are arranged chronologically by the date of each crash. They were prepared from German sources (see the next entry, Record Group 242) by the Notification Section. Information in each record includes the time of the crash, the type of craft, craft identification numbers or symbols (if available), the location of the crash, and reference numbers from pertinent German records. The list pertains mostly to British and American aircraft.

Record Group 242   National Archives Collection of Foreign Records Seized

III.26 The Records of *Luftgaukommandos* (Air Defense Commands) are part of the German records seized by the United States during and after World War II. They include records of commands responsible for defense against air attacks, such as German antiaircraft units, and contain accounts of American, British, and Russian aircraft downed and the fate of their crews. Since downed fliers who survived and were captured only passed through the hands of those who served in Luftgaukommandos, these records are of limited use with respect to POWs. They should be used in support of the Missing Air Crew Reports (see paragraphs **III.23** and **III.24**). The MACRs sometimes contain references to the records of the *Luftgaukommandos,* and may include English translations of the German-language documents. In any case, the researcher seeking information on an American POW should consult the records of the *Luftgaukommandos* only if he or she has a specific interest in the loss of an aircraft, or if it is impossible to find information on the POW using more complete records, such as those in Record Groups 389, 331, 153, and 407.

III.27 The information most often given about individual downed airmen is name, rank, date and place of crash, and his fate (capture, injury, death, etc.). There are four indexes accompanying the records of *Luftgaukommandos.* Two are arranged alphabetically by the surnames of downed fliers. Another is arranged by the date of the plane crash. The fourth is geographic, but it is of limited usefulness because it is ordered according to Luftwaffe administrative districts.

RECORDS OF ESCAPE AND EVASION

Record Group 319   Records of the Army Staff

III.28   Among the records of the Far Eastern Branch of the Assistant Chief of Staff, G-2 (Intelligence), is a **numerical series of intelligence documents ("ID File"), June 1944–1945** (3,930 ft.). Within the series are 3 feet of "escape and evasion reports, Far East" (ID #912440). There are approximately 200 such reports that concern the activities of U.S. military personnel (and some civilians) as they sought to evade capture or to escape from enemy custody during World War II. The reports are filed in alphabetical order by the surname of the subject person. Some contain follow-up material such as newspaper clippings and copies of other publications. It appears that these records overlap in coverage with those of SCAP (see Record Group 331, **III.7–III.9**).

Record Group 332   Records of U.S. Theaters of War, World War II

III.29   Escape and evasion reports, European Theater of Operations, consist of approximately 3,700 reports that concern the activities of U.S. military personnel (and some civilians) as they sought to evade capture or to escape from enemy custody during World War II. The reports are arranged by report number, but have a name index. They were collected for the purpose of studying escape methods and the behavior of captured American military personnel, apparently with the aim of improving training.

III.30   There are also files on "helpers," foreign nationals who assisted Americans in their efforts at escape and evasion. These files are arranged generally by the name of the country in which the action took place, thereunder by "class" of helper, and thereunder alphabetically by the surnames of helpers. The helpers are classed from I to IV in descending order of the risk they incurred or the sacrifice they made in their actions. Most of those in class I, for example, paid with imprisonment or their lives. There are exceptions to this hierarchy among the records that are relevant to particular countries. Two indexes to these records exist: one arranged alphabetically by the surnames of helpers; the other arranged alphabetically by the surnames of the Americans who received assistance.

III.31   The researcher should remember that these records are of limited usefulness regarding POWs. They address many Americans who were not POWs; and only a small percentage of POWs attempted escape and evasion and reported on it. It is important to realize that part of the series is still classified, and that the records are likely to be arranged somewhat differently for each country. In short, this series should be used either after failing to find information in other record groups, or to supplement or cross-check information derived from other record groups.

Record Group 247   Records of the Office of the Chief of Chaplains

III.32   Records kept by and about chaplains contain some information on American POWs and civilian detainees. Such information is found in the files of chaplains who were themselves POWs, or who served POWs. Thus, with one exception, it is necessary to know a chaplain's name to locate information on individuals in these records.

III.33   The **chaplain monthly report files, 1917–1950** (871 ft.), are arranged in four chronological block subseries. The one for 1920–45 is arranged by Reserve (670 ft.) and then Regular Army (34 ft.), and thereunder alphabetically by the surname of the chaplain. Interspersed with the monthly reports are copies of correspondence and material constituting the relevant chaplain's personnel file. The reports are on forms that account for the number of services, hospital visits, counseling sessions, teaching sessions, births/christenings, marriages, and funerals the chaplain conducted. The quality of the reports varies, as does the amount and quality of correspondence. The forms left latitude for a wide range of personal styles in reporting.

III.34   One series by which a researcher might find information with only a POW's name is the **index to chaplains reports, 1923–55** (274 ft.), which consists of 3- by 5-inch cards. It is an index to the funerals reported in the foregoing series, arranged alphabetically by the surnames of the deceased. Each card contains the name of the deceased individual, the name of the chaplain, and the date of the chaplain's monthly report in which the funeral is accounted for. Since a few chaplains were POWs, the services they performed while they were held captive are recorded in these reports.

III.35   The series **general correspondence, 1920–53** (170 ft.), of the Office of the Chief of Chaplains is arranged into four subseries by chronological blocks, and thereunder by the War Department decimal classification scheme. The first subseries is for the period 1920-45 (114 ft.). It contains, under decimal 383.6, "Prisoners of war," a small file of correspondence (2 in.) pertaining mostly to chaplains who were POWs; but it also has information on civilian religious workers, including clergy, who were detainees.

Part IV

<u>Postwar POW Records</u>

IV.1   The records described in this section were created or put into their final form after the end of World War II in attempts to account for all American POWs or civilian internees. They are essentially lists, and therefore contain little information beyond what is necessary to identify an individual.

Record Group 24   Records of the Bureau of Naval Personnel

IV.2   Among the records of BUPERS Casualty Section is the series **World War II casualty lists and related records** (13 ft.). It contains one list of value in identifying individual POWs— "Complete List of Prisoners of War, 28 October 1946," that presumably includes only Navy personnel. The volume is arranged into separate lists of officers and enlisted men; thereunder separated by "active" and "inactive" designations; and thereunder by the labels "classified as survivors" and "classified as dead." The lists contain each individual's name and rank, a "file number," and an "area number." (The last two are presumably locators).

Record Group 38   Records of the Office of the Chief of Naval Operations

IV.3   Among the records of the Bureau of Medicine and Surgery is a set of records collected from Bilibid Prison [Philippines] and the Hospital Corps Archives [1941–71] (4 ft.). It consists of papers salvaged from the Bilibid Prison Hospital and related documents drawn together by the Bureau of Medicine and Surgery over a 10-year period. Included are administrative and medical files from the hospital; diaries and personal accounts from individuals who were there during the war; monographs, publications, and other papers on topics related to Bilibid; and some lists and other material on a few other Japanese-controlled hospitals and POW camps. A box list for the records is available.

Record Group 407   Records of the Adjutant General's Office, 1917–

IV.4   Part of the records of the Strength and Accounting Branch of the Adjutant General's Office is the series **strength returns, 1941–June 1954**. At the end of the series are 26 bound volumes, completed in the early 1950s, that list U.S. military personnel who were POWs or missing in action during World War II. They generally are presented in columns that include at least the person's name, service number, rank, and service. Some volumes contain handwritten annotations.

1. Vols. 1-23. Alphabetical Listing of Prisoners of War, World War II, Including U.S. Army and U.S. Air Force Personnel. CFN-208. List [see below]. The Adjutant General's Office. Strength Accounting Branch, 20 February 1950. These volumes are generally arranged alphabetically by the surname of the former POW. The separate volumes are "Lists":

A	H	P
B	I	Q–R
B–V, Additional Lists	J	S
C	K	T
D	L	U–V
E	M	W
F	N	X,Y,Z
G	O	

2. Vol. 24. Alphabetical Listing of Current Missing in Action as Prepared by Machine Records Branch, Mediterranean Theater of Operations, European Theater of Operations, Africa Middle East Theater, as of 3 July 1945. CFN-69. This volume contains only surnames "Aaron" through "Laing." There are handwritten annotations on many of the entries.

3. Vol. 25. Deceased American Prisoners of War Held by the German Government. CFN-74. This volume contains the full alphabetic run of surnames.

4. Vol. 26. American Prisoners of War Held by the German Government Unaccounted For. CFN-74. This volume contains the full alphabetic run of surnames. Many entries include handwritten annotations.

REFERENCE MATERIAL ON WORLD WAR II POWS

IV.5   The following volumes contain lists of American military personnel who died or were declared missing in World War II, some of whom died while in enemy hands. They are not part of the accessioned records of NARA, but are part of the reference collection of the textual reference staff of the National Archives at College Park, MD.

1. World War II Honor List of Dead and Missing—State of [. . .]. War Department, June 1946. These publications include American military personnel who died while in enemy hands. There is a separate volume for each state and the District of Columbia, and another for territories and protectorates. Entries are filed according to the home address of the deceased or missing person. Each volume is arranged by county and thereunder alphabetically by surname, and lists the person's name, rank, service, service number, and status.

2. War Casualties: Officers, U.S. Navy and U.S. Naval Reserve, 7 December 1941–1 January 1944, Bureau of Naval Personnel (1944). These lists contain full name, rank, serial number, and address of next of kin. Persons who died while prisoners of war are included. The volume is arranged in three sections:

a. all casualties listed alphabetically by surname;

b. casualties due to enemy action, divided into categories by type of service and/or action and thereunder listed alphabetically by surname; and

c. casualties not due to enemy action, divided into categories and thereunder listed alphabetically by surname.

3. State Summary of War Casualties ([name of state]), United States Navy (1946). These lists also contain full name, rank, serial number, and address of next of kin. There is a separate volume for each state and the District of Columbia, and another for all U.S. territories and protectorates. Each volume is divided into casualties listed by county, and thereunder arranged alphabetically by surname.

4. Chronological History and Pertinent Facts Pertaining to U.S. Military Internees in Sweden During World War II, NWCTM Reference Collection #43. This volume contains a list of individual airmen interned in Sweden during the war.

Part V

Other Records

V.1   There are other records of interest to researchers seeking information on the personal experience of an American who was a POW or a civilian internee in World War II. All of them are of less value in that search than are the records described in the preceeding three sections of this reference information paper. In some cases this is because these "other records" are far from comprehensive in their approach to even a portion of one particular branch of the U.S. military service. That is true, for example, of the press releases described below. Other records were produced purposely to offer a picture of military or POW experience that, although it depicts individuals, was intended to represent the whole with the aim of inspiring the nation or capturing a sample of the American wartime experience.

V.2   Some records contain images of individual POWs who are not identified, but could possibly be identified given some special knowledge or preliminary research. A few photographic records are accompanied by name indexes or other finding aids that could enable a researcher with a little background information to find an image of a given individual. While these records are of great value in a few cases, they are considered to be "other records" in this reference information paper because the appearance of a given individual in them is the result of serendipity and not some consistent plan on the part of the persons who created the records.

V.3   This section is organized by record type or media, with press releases first, followed by motion pictures, sound recordings, and still pictures. Within each type, descriptions are arranged in order by record group number.[4]

PRESS RELEASES

Record Group 337   Records of Headquarters Army Ground Forces

V.4   Army Ground Forces was the command structure in charge of organizing and training all American ground combat forces in World War II. The Information Section of the Office of the Commanding General, Army Ground Forces produced **press releases, 1943–45** (9 ft.), that are arranged by date (often several per day) and bound in manila folders. Each press release contains the names of publications to which the item was sent. On the covers of the manila folders are lists of the subjects of the press releases, ordered the same as the contents. The subject usually consists of the name of the individual who is the focus of the article, but a few articles concern several individuals who are receiving the same award or class of award.

V.5   The simplest and briefest releases are notices of individual soldiers returning home on leave, telling their plans to visit relatives (who are often named), details about their civilian lives, and details about their military service. There are many interviews with servicemen recounting combat and other military experiences. Numerous articles are about combat deaths and heroism. A relatively small number of the press releases are about individuals who were POWs during the war.

MOTION PICTURES

V.6   There is a relatively large number of scenes of American POWs and civilian internees on motion picture film for the World War II period. For the most part this footage consists of a few minutes in each instance, and there is no systematic way to track down or even identify individuals. However, there are usually clues regarding the approximate time and the location at which the pictures were taken. So the possibility exists that persons who were imprisoned, their family members, or others familiar with them can select motion pictures based on knowledge of someone's experience as a POW or civilian internee and have some chance of finding film of an identifiable individual. Therefore, with minor exceptions, the descriptions of films in this reference information paper will consist of identifying information and the available clues about the time and location at which they were shot. They will be listed in order by record group number and thereunder by the NARA identification number. Much of the material, especially the newsreels, is subject to copyright or other restrictions regarding reproduction.

Record Group 18   Records of the Army Air Forces

V.7   Records of the Army Air Forces Combat Film Library contain some footage relevant to the experiences of captured Americans in World War II. For instance 18 CS 3137-2 through 18 CS 3137-8 show various scenes related to the conditions in and liberation of the "Santo Tomas Concentration Camp" near Manila in the Philippines.

Record Group 56   General Records of the Department of the Treasury

V.8   The Department of the Treasury sponsored films to promote the sale of war bonds. Two contain footage of American POWs:

1. 56.30 "My Japan" (1943?). Depiction of the Japanese war effort using captured film that includes shots of American POWs. (sound, black & white, 35 mm & 16 mm)

2. 56.34.1 "New Philippine News" (1944?). Undernourished American POWs and the graves of prisoners found when the Philippines were recaptured. (sound, black & white, 16 mm)

V.9   Films in the Office of the Secretary of War were created under the auspices of the Allied Military Governments in Europe and the Far East. All but one, which is described last, are short scenes interspersed with other subjects. Unless otherwise noted, all are black & white, 35 mm, with sound.

1. 107.66 [Belfort Gap Region] (1944). Smashed American tanks and POWs marched to the rear and questioned (captured footage).

2. 107.787 [Allied Prisoners in Paris] (1944). A long column of British and U.S. POWs marched through Paris under German guard (silent).

3. 107.848 "The German Army in Action" (1944). Reel 2: Wreckage of downed Allied planes and captured pilots; Allied prisoners marched to the rear past wrecked equipment and vehicles.

4. 107.915 "The German Army in Action" (1944). Reels 1, 3, and 5: U.S. prisoners marched to the rear. Reel 6: Captured U.S. pilots questioned. Reel 8: Allied prisoners marched to the rear past smashed allied vehicles and equipment.

5. 107.1542 [Mission to Manchuria] (1945). Former Japanese prison guards and liberated Allied POWs at a Japanese prison camp in Manchuria.

V.10   The public relations records of the Office of the Secretary of War contain **motion picture film released to the newsreel room, 1942–45** (191 reels): Among the stories is [American POWs Freed in the Philippines] (107.1041) consisting of 3 reels (43 min.) of black and white silent film of the liberation of a group of American POWs. The visual narrative proceeds from American and Filipino troops finding and liberating an unidentified camp, through the transport of the former POWs to a processing center, and culminates in their processing, including issuance of new uniforms, interviews, and candid shots of activities such as haircuts, mess, and debriefing.

V.11   There are numerous clear long, medium, and close-up shots of individuals, including former POWs, Filipino nationals, and American processors and liberators. There are 9 interviews in which unidentified former POWs are on camera for 45 seconds to 3 minutes each in full frontal shots from the chest up. Although there is no sound extant for the film, these are clear shots and lip movement is very discernible. Also, although there is no identification of the camp or camps, there are apparently two processing centers filmed. One has a building labeled "Cuimba [or Guimba] East Central School," and the other a building labeled "92nd Evacuation Hospital."

Record Group 111   Records of the Office of the Chief Signal Officer

V.12   The Signal Corps, administered by the Chief Signal Officer, was responsible for communications within and by the U.S. Army, and was charged with production of Army training films. The corps also had overall responsibility for motion picture production in the War Department.

1. 111 ADC Consists of unedited footage, including a relatively large amount on POWs. A card index to the file contains more than 120 entries under the heading "Prisoners of War, Allied," most of which include Americans. The majority are shots of POWs at, or shortly after, liberation; and most of the cards indicate the site and date on which the film was taken. (silent, black & white, 35 mm & 16 mm)

2. 111 CB 18 "Combat Bulletin No. 18: Progress in Southern France" (St. Raphael), (1944). Reel 2: U.S. prisoners gathered into groups. (sound, black & white, 35 mm & 16 mm)

3. 111 CR 4 "Combat Report No. 4: Appointment in Tokyo" (1945). Reel 4: A patrol liberates U.S. and Filipino POWs. (sound, black & white, 35 mm)

4. 111 M 1173 "The Army Nurse" (1945). Nurses who were POWs. (sound, black & white, 35 mm)

5. 111 M 1211 "The True Glory" (1945). Made in cooperation with the British Ministry of Information; covers the Allied invasion and conquest of Western Europe. Reel 9: The liberation of U.S. prisoners. (sound, black & white, 35 mm)

6. 111 OF 15 "Orientation Film No. 15: Our Job in Japan" (1946). Reel 2: U.S. troops in a Japanese prison camp. (sound, black & white, 35 mm)

7. 111 OF 26 "Orientation Film No. 26: This Is the Philippines" (1945). Reel 1: The surrender of U.S. troops and massed prisoners. (sound, black & white, 35 mm)

8. 111 SFR 43 "Activities in European Theater of Operations [etc.]" (1945). Reel 3: U.S. Rangers and Filipinos set out for and return from a raid on a Japanese prison camp; the rescued inmates recount experiences and receive aid. (sound, black & white, 35 mm & 16 mm)

9. 111 SFR 44 "Invasion of Iwo Jima [etc.]" (1945). Reel 3: Former inmates of Cabanatuan Prison recount cruelty. Reel 4: U.S. students at Santo Tomas University and former inmates of Bilibid Prison prepare to return to the United States (sound, black & white, 35 mm & 16 mm)

10. 111 SM 5 "The War No. 5 (Screen Magazine No. 5)" (1943). Reel 1: An Army nurse relates her experiences on Corregidor; U.S. prisoners on Bataan. (sound, black & white, 35 mm)

11. 111 SM 41 "Army-Navy Screen Magazine, No. 41" (1944). Reel 1: Liberated U.S. flyers board planes at an airfield near Bucharest for a flight to Bari, Italy. (sound, black & white, 35 mm)

12. 111 SM 52 "Army-Navy Screen Magazine, No. 52" (1945). Reel 1: Ex-POWs after the liberation of a Japanese prison camp in the Philippines; they describe the Bataan Death March. (sound, black & white, 35 mm)

13. 111 SM 58 "Army-Navy Screen Magazine, No. 58" (1945). Reel 1: A U.S. soldier loses an arm during an aerial attack on Corregidor, is imprisoned in Cabanatuan, rescued, and taken to the United States; General Wainwright's surrender of Corregidor, the Bataan Death March, prison scenes at Cabanatuan, the release of U.S. POWs by Filipino guerrillas and U.S. troops, transports carry released prisoners to the United States, and former prisoners reunited with their families. (sound, black & white, 35 mm.)

14. 111 SM 68 "Surrender in the Pacific (Screen Magazine No. 68)" (1945). Reel 2: U.S. POWs released from prisons in Tokyo. (sound, black & white, 35 mm)

15. 111 SM 79 "On the Air (Screen Magazine No. 79)" (1945). Reel 2: The delousing of recently released U.S. POWs in Germany. (sound, black & white, 35 mm)

16. 111 WF 42 "A Report on German Morale (War Film No. 42)" (1945). Made in cooperation with the Office of Strategic Services. Reel 1: Brief shots of U.S. POWs. (sound, black & white, 35 mm)

Record Group 153   Records of the Office of the Judge Advocate General (Army)

V.13   The case file concerning case No. 16-149, *United States* v. *Lt. Gen. Kurt Maelzer*, the former German commander of Rome, contains the 3-minute silent motion picture "Rome March." The U.S. prosecutors were investigating allegations of the forced march of American POWs in 1944.

Record Group 208   Records of the Office of War Information

V.14   The Office of War Information coordinated the dissemination of news about the war to the American public. Its activities included work on feature films as well as newsreels.

1. 208 UN.145 "New Fighter Plane Flies 'Tail First' [etc.]." United News (1945). General MacArthur is in attendance as civilians are liberated from prison camps in Manila. (sound, black & white, 35 mm)

2. 208 UN.171A "Allied Forces Land in Japan." United News (1945). American prisoners released from prisons in Japan. (sound, black & white, 35 mm)

3. 208 UN.172 "First Pictures Inside Bomb Blasted Japan [etc]." United News (1945). Americans liberated from Japanese prison camps. (sound, black & white, 35 mm)

4. 208 UN.173 "Japanese Surrender More Territory [etc.]." United News (1945). American POWs leave Japanese prison camps. (sound, black & white, 35 mm)

Record Group 242   National Archives Collection of Foreign Records Seized

V.15 Motion picture films were among the records seized by the United States during World War II. They include German, Japanese, and Italian films, both feature productions and newsreels.

GERMAN FOOTAGE

V.16 Several of the captured German newsreels include brief shots of American POWs. Most of the scenes are of captured ground forces being interrogated, searched, or led away to prison. Exceptions to these kinds of scenes are noted. All of the film is sound, black and white, 35 mm. Most of the narration is in German, with a few items overdubbed in English and a few in Portuguese.

1. 242.266   (1944)   Reel 1.

2. 242.268   (1944)   Captured U.S. pilots.

3. 242.272   (1944)   Captured Allied airmen.

4. 242.278   (1944)   Captured American pilots.

5. 242.283   (1944)   Reel 2.

6. 242.291   (1944)   Reel 2: American POWs marched through Paris as French civilians kick and strike them.

7. 242.320   (1944)   Reel 2.

8. 242.314   (1944)   Reel 2.

9. 242.308   (1942)   Reel 2: American POWs near a crossroads in Flanders.

10. 242 GN 103   (1944)   Reel 2: U.S. pilot bails out of a damaged aircraft; U.S. pilots interrogated.

11. 242 GN 114   (1944)   Reel 2: U.S. and British prisoners; U.S. prisoners carry a wounded comrade.

12. 242 MID 2740   (1944)   Captured American paratroopers.

13.	242 MID 2743	(1944)	Reel 2.
14.	242 MID 2752	(1944)	Reel 2: French civilians mistreat Allied POWs as they are marched through Paris.
15.	242 MID 2766	(1944)	Reel 2: captured pilots.
16.	242 MID 2769	(1944)	Reel 2.
17.	242 MID 2926	(1944?)	Reel 2: British and American troops in German POW camp.
18.	242 MID 3136	(1945)	Reels 1 and 2.
19.	242 MID 3200	(1945)	Reel 1: exchange of German and U.S. prisoners; Reel 2.
20.	242 MID 3420	(1944)	Allied POWs marched through the streets of Paris by German guards and are struck, spit on, and tripped by French civilians. Close shots of individual prisoners and a panorama of prisoners massed in a square.
21.	242 MID 3543	(1944)	U.S. pilots taken prisoner.
22.	242 MID 3689	(1944)	Reel 2.
23.	242 MID 3707	(1944)	Reel 1: U.S. prisoners marched through the streets of Rome; shore guns destroy a U.S. landing craft and capture the wounded survivors; U.S., British, and East Indian prisoners are taken.
24.	242 MID 6122	(1944)	Reel 2.
25.	242 MID 6137	(1944?)	Reel 2: U.S. prisoners taken near Luneville, France.
26.	242 MID 6140	(1943?)	Reel 2.
27.	242 MID 6141	(1944?)	Reel 2: U.S. 82d Airborne and 8th Infantry Division troops captured near Caen, Normandy.
28.	242 MID 6199	(1944)	U.S. soldiers taken prisoner near Cassino, Italy.

29. 242 MID 2619 "Gironale di guerra (War Journal) No. 310" (1943). U.S. troops captured in Tunisia. (sound, black & white, 35 mm)

30. 242 MID 3260 "La settimana Europea (This week's events in Europe)" (1944). Wounded German and U.S. prisoners exchanged. (sound, black & white, 35 mm)

JAPANESE FOOTAGE

31. 242 MID 2087 "Tokyo No Gaika (The victory song of the Orient)" (1942). Depicts the Japanese invasion and occupation of the Philippines in 1942. Reel 7: U.S. and Filipino troops surrender and are marched to the rear. Reel 9: U.S. POWs on Corregidor take salt tablets and eat at field kitchen; general shots of U.S. POWs. Reel 11: Generals Wainwright and Beebe attend surrender conference with General Homma. Reel 12: American POWs are treated in underground hospital and eat in mess hall. Reel 13: American POWs on Corregidor, including Army nurses; closeups of Colonel Bowler and Generals Beebe, Wainwright, and Moore. (sound, black & white, 35 mm)

32. 242 MID 3278 "Bataan and Corregidor" (1942). U.S. prisoners by a bridge. (sound, black & white, 35 mm)

33. 242 MID 3280 "American surrender at Manila" (1942). General Wainwright and other officers sign surrender documents; general shots of American prisoners. (sound, black & white, 35 mm)

Record Group 331   Records of Allied Operational and Occupation Headquarters, World War II

V.17 Motion picture film in this record group includes:

1. 331.2 [POWs in the Philippines, 1941-45] (1947). Scenes of POWs and camps prepared for the War Crimes Commission and authenticated with a filmed affidavit by the Legal Branch, Prosecution Section, U.S. Army. (sound, black & white)

2. 331.3 [POW Interviews, Sept. 11-12, 1945]. Brief, unedited sound interviews with American POWs recounting their treatment in captivity, followed by silent scenes of camps, camp activities, religious services, and additional silent scenes of interviews. (sound & silent, black & white)

3. 331.3 Captured Japanese Film (n.d.). A crashed B-24; 8 American airmen being interrogated. (sound, color, 16 mm)

V.18   The motion pictures in this record group focus primarily on liberated concentration camps in Europe, but the following titles contain footage of POWs.

1. 338.006 "POW Camp Liberated." (sound, black & white, 16 mm)

2. 338.027 "General Eisenhower and Soldiers, in Concentration Camp." (sound, black & white, 16 mm)

3. 338.029 "American Prisoners Released." (sound, black & white, 16 mm)

4. 338.037 "Military Personnel." (sound, black & white, 16 mm)

5. 338.044 "Liberated Soldiers." (sound, black & white, 16 mm)

NATIONAL ARCHIVES COLLECTION OF DONATED MATERIALS

V.19   The National Archives and Records Administration is authorized by law to accept from private sources documents—including motion pictures, sound recordings, and still pictures—that offer evidence of the U.S. Government's organization, functions, policies, decisions, procedures, and transactions. The materials in this collection have been donated by a wide range of businesses, cultural organizations, institutions, and individuals.

1. 200.362 *Die Deutsche Wochenschau* (The German Weekly Newsreel) (1944). German troops advance against American forces and take prisoners. (sound, black & white, 16 mm)

2. 200 PN 2.73 *Paramount News* [May 8] (1943). U.S. troops surrender on Corregidor. (sound, black & white, 35 mm)

3. 200 PN 3.45 *Paramount News* [Feb. 2] (1944). The surrender of Corregidor and the Bataan Death March; a memorial by an American POW's hometown; and a post card from an American prisoner on Luzon. (sound, black & white, 35 mm)

4. 200 PN 4.47 *Paramount News* [Feb. 9] (1945). Former U.S. POWs deplane at LaGuardia Field, New York, and tell of experiences in Japanese and German POW camps. (sound, black & white, 35 mm)

5. 200 PN 4.57 *Paramount News* [Mar. 16] (1945). Survivors of Cabanatuan Prison Camp disembark in San Francisco; U.S. POWs herded into barbed wire enclosures on Corregidor (captured footage). (sound, black & white, 35 mm)

6. 200 PN 4.58 *Paramount News* [Mar. 20] (1945). U.S. naval officers freed from Bilibid and the grave of those who died there. (sound, black & white, 35 mm)

7. 200 PN 4.76 *Paramount News* [May 23] (1945). Parisians assault Allied POWs during German occupation. (sound, black & white, 35 mm)

8. 200 PN 5.6 *Paramount News* [Sept. 19] (1945). U.S. POWs liberated from Nissen No. 2 and Omori camps in Japan. (sound, black & white, 35 mm)

9. 200 PN 5.9 *Paramount News* [Sept. 29] (1945). U.S. POWs released and Japanese guards imprisoned at Mukden, Manchuria, camp. (sound, black & white, 35 mm)

SOUND RECORDINGS

V.20   The following entries are examples of records concerning the experiences of American captives during World War II that may be found among the extensive collection of sound recordings in the National Archives.

Record Group 238   National Archives Collection of World War II War Crimes Records

V.21   NARA has sound recordings of the entire proceedings of the International Military Tribunal, Nuernberg, November 20, 1945–October 1, 1946, and copies of those recordings that were introduced as evidence before the tribunal. See **III.13–III.14** for a description of the textual records of the tribunal.

Record Group 262   Records of the Foreign Broadcast Intelligence Service

V.22   The Foreign Broadcast Intelligence Service (FBIS) was established by the Federal Communications Commission in February 1941 to record, translate, and analyze foreign radio broadcasts and to report on them to interested U.S. Government agencies. FBIS was transferred to the War Department in December 1945 and placed under the Military Intelligence Division of the General Staff.

V.23   NARA has a collection of more than 20,000 radio programs from FBIS. Some of these are shortwave broadcasts by Radio Tokyo and Radio Berlin during World War II in which English-speaking announcers such as "Tokyo Rose" gave the names of, and information about, American POWs.

Record Group 338   Records of U.S. Army Commands, 1942–

V.24   The records of the Judge Advocate Division contain four sound recordings of testimony, statements, and eyewitness reports concerning the murder of U.S. prisoners of war (May–December 1944).

Record Group 80   General Records of the Department of the Navy, 1789–1947

V.25   The **general photographic file of the Department of Navy, 1900–58** (80-G) consists of approximately 700,000 images (prints and negatives) covering a great variety of subjects. Most of the images have very informative captions. The series is arranged numerically by item number, but is accompanied by two thorough indexes. The general index (80-GG) was created by the Department of Navy and consists of approximately 800,000 3- by 5-inch cards arranged into two sections, 1942-45 and 1946-58. Each of the sections has three subsections that are arranged (1) numerically by ship hull number; (2) numerically by aircraft number; and (3) alphabetically by subject. The third (subject) subsection in the World War II section contains more than 4 inches of index cards related to American POWs. The major entries are "Prison Camps" (.5 in.), "Prisoners of War" (.75 in.), and "Prisoners-American" (2.25 in.). There is also a large "personalities" (name) index (80-GX) to the individuals identified in the photographs throughout the series.

V.26   Nearly all of the Navy photographs pertaining to American POWs deal with Japanese camps. This is obviously because the Navy's role in the Pacific theater of war was relatively larger than in the European. Specific camps and geographic locations are identified in most of the captions. A few captions bear the names of individual POWs.

Record Group 111   Records of the Office of the Chief Signal Officer

V.27   The series **Signal Corps photographs of American military activity, ca. 1754–1954** (111-SC), contains approximately 386,000 items covering a very large variety of military and related subjects. There are finding aids to the series that offer access to general topics, but the best method of access is through the use of another series, **U.S. Army Signal Corps photographs of military activity during World War II and the Korean Conflict, 1941–54** (111-SCA), which consists of 6,760 albums of photographs. These albums contain images selected by the Signal Corps to best represent significant subjects and subtopics in the photograph collection. A third series, **index to U.S. Army Signal Corps black-and-white photographs in series 111-SC, ca. 1900–81** (111-SCY), provides general access to 111-SC, but the best route to pictures of POWs is to consult the title list for the albums in series 111-SCA.

V.28   There are 62 albums of photographs (each consisting of about 1.5 inches of prints) with POWs as their subject. These albums are arranged under three general headings: "Prisoners," "Prisoners Released," and "Prisoners Repatriated." They are arranged thereunder alphabetically by the nationality of the POWs. Some albums are arranged thereunder by the country in which the POW was liberated. Since some of the albums are of photographs from the Korean Conflict, and many are of Allied and Axis prisoners of World War II, only the 7 albums below concern American POWs in World War II. A few photographs of civilian internees are scattered among those of military prisoners.

1. 4911   "Prisoners/American"

2. 4957   "Prisoners Released/American/[in] Bulgaria, France, and Italy"

3. 4958   "Prisoners Released/American/[in] Germany"

4. 4959   "Prisoners Released/American/[in] Japan"

5. 4960   "Prisoners Released/American/[in] Japan"

6. 4963   "Prisoners Released/American/[in the] Philippine Islands"

7. 4964   "Prisoners Released/American/[in the] Philippine Islands"

There is a chance of finding pictures of individual POWs by knowing the country by or in which they were held or liberated. In a few cases the captions accompanying the photographs reveal the names and/or units of individuals. Also, many of the images show the faces of POWs clearly. While these cases represent very few individuals relative to the entire population of American POWs, it might be possible to locate an individual, given a good amount of background information such as date of release, camp in which held, and location of repatriation.

Record Group 127   Records of the U.S. Marine Corps

V.29   There are relatively few Marine Corps photographs of American POWs. The only series for which access to such shots is relatively easy is **photographs of Marine Corps activities taken in the United States and foreign countries, ca. 1939–1958** (127-GC). A box list for the some 41,000 photographs reveals the subject and geographic headings by which the series is arranged. The images of American POWs total only 12 in 2 boxes (numbers 7 and 10). They are all pictures taken of Marines several days or weeks after their repatriation. Most of them include captions with individual names. All were captives in the Philippines, mostly at Cabanatuan or Palawan.

Record Group 319   Records of the Army Staff

V.30   An album of photographic prints, "A Glimpse Into the P.O.W. Camps of Formosa" [1943–44]" (319-PW), was probably made by Japanese officials to show favorable conditions in five POW camps on Formosa (Taiwan). Included are pictures of prisoners engaged in animal husbandry and recreational activities and participating in religious services. Also shown are several Allied military and civilian prisoners, including Lieutenant General Jonathan Wainwright. The photographs are of good quality and include clear shots of the faces of several unidentified American POWs.

V.31   Photographs used to defend Japanese prison camp staff who were accused of war crimes comprise the series **photographs of American servicemen in Japanese POW camps, ca. 1945** (200-K). There are 35 prints of photographs taken in camps around Tokyo (Omori, Niigata, Sendai, Yokohama, Kawasaki, and Tokyo Main Camp). The photographs were donated to the National Archives by Mr. Ira Kaye, who used them while a member of the Judge Advocate General's Corps. No Americans are identified by name, but there are several shots in which the faces of many American and Allied prisoners are clear. Some 80 percent of the photographs were taken by Japanese during the war, and many appear to be staged. A few were taken by staff of the Army Signal Corps after the end of the war.

End notes

[1] A copy of this file has been converted to computer magnetic tape (see **II.11** and **II.14–16**).

[2] A copy of this file has been converted to computer magnetic tape (see **II.11** and **II.14–16**).

[3] The use of the term "201" to label this and the following series is based on the War Department decimal classification scheme, which assigned all individuals' official personnel files to decimal category 201. From that usage grew the custom of referring to any file containing personal information about an individual as a "201 file." This custom applies only to the files of organizations under the aegis of the War Department and has never been used to designate files in the Department of the Navy.

[4] The still photographic records of the Office of War Information (RG 208), while voluminous, are practically useless for the purpose of identifying individual Americans other than well-known personalities. They also consist largely of material collected from other sources, and thus relevant images are likely to be more easily available elsewhere.

Appendix A

Box List for general subject file, 1942–46
American POW Information Bureau, Records Branch
Records of the Office of the Provost Marshal General, 1941-
Record Group 389

A.1 The series **correspondence, camp reports, diaries, rosters, and other records relating to Americans interned by Germany and Japan during World War II, 1942–46**, contains files arranged alphabetically by subjects. Some of the subject categories are geographic locations, some are record types, some are indicators of content, and still others are based on other concepts. Because of the inconsistencies in these subject headings, this box list for the series is offered as a guide to the general contents of the records. Since records can be reboxed relatively often in the processes of preservation and holdings maintenance, this list is no more than that—a simple guide to the general contents of the records; not a key to the exact locations of specific records.

A.2 The heading adjacent to each box number is the information found on the box label; any information that follows is a brief description of the contents of the box. It should be noted that these descriptions were written with the intention of highlighting information on personal experience during World War II and might be of limited value for unrelated research topics.

A.3 Preservation work on this series led to the addition of several boxes after the records were organizationally processed. The new boxes were given the number of the box preceding them with the suffix "A" added. Gaps in the box numbering system are indicated in the "Box No." column.

	Box	Contents
A.4	2069	A.C. Crew to American Red Cross Generally records based on International Red Cross efforts to identify POWs held by both Germany and Japan—correspondence, reports, lists.
	2069A	American Red Cross, 1942–43
A.5	2070–2071	Archive File 3100-5a to Army Personnel List Lists of deceased POWs and some returned to military control (RMC); some include next of kin with addresses. All are of POWs held by the Japanese.
A.6	2072–2074	Aviators: Crash Victims Books with entries arranged alphabetically by surname, containing

name, service number(?), rank, and a code number(?). Only crashes that occurred [in the] ETO are included.

A.7 2075   Aviators: Index Crash Location Unknown
Contains no names.

A.8 2076–2108   Bern Dispatches [#1–12420] to Bern, Miscellaneous
Diplomatic correspondence, arranged in numerical order by dispatch number (roughly chronological), concerning POW information and inquiries.

A.9 2109   Bilibid Hospital List to Cabanatuan Prison Camp
These are the files that follow the last Bern dispatches. They contain several lists, arranged alphabetically by surname, of POWs and civilian internees in the Philippines.

A.10 2110–2118A   Cables, U.S. #1–3300
Diplomatic correspondence and inquiries concerning POWs. Many have columnized, alphabetized name lists attached. There is some information on wounds that may by exempt from disclosure, but the information is generally quite sketchy.

A.11 2119   Cable Copy List to Cables: Vatican
The "cable copy list" is of lists that were sent through Switzerland of POWs held by the Japanese. The Vatican cables are numbered 127-287, with about 50 missing, and were sent to the Apostolic Delegate in Washington, DC. They are roughly chronological from October 1941 to November 1944. Many have been tabbed for censorship.

A.12 2120–2135   Camps: Burma-Thailand-Siam to Camps: Wake Island; Camp Moves: Germany and Japan
See Appendix B for an index to this subject category arranged alphabetically by geographic area and location. See the text of the series description (**II.5–II.10**) for information on record content.

A.13 2136–2138   Camp Lists: Germany . . . .
These files consist of POW lists received from German authorities during the war. Nearly all are on German forms and convey little information that is not in the card index of prisoners. They are arranged alphanumerically by the German abbreviations for the camps, which was based on a "type name." For example, STG stands for *Stammlager* or *Stalag*—"base camp" (a general camp). DULAG stands for *Durchgangslager*—"processing center." Each abbreviation is followed by a numeric or alphanumeric indicator for specific camp sites.

Box	Contents

2151   Camp Reports: **Germany–STALAG (Enlisted Men), STG 13-D to 398

2152–2152A   Camp Reports: Greece to Italy
Contains Greece, Hungary, and **Italy.

2153   Camp Reports: **Italy to **Japan

2154   Camp Reports: **Japan to **Philippine Islands
Contains **Japan, Korea, Malaya, Manchuria, and **Philippine Islands. The last file includes a report of more than 100 pages filed in November 1945 on the POW situation in the Philippines during the war. It contains illustrations, analysis, narrative, and details on some camp locations.

2155   Camp Reports: **Rumania to **Thailand
Contains **Rumania, Switzerland, Thailand, Siam, and Yugoslavia.

2155A   Camp Reports: **Yugoslavia

A.15 2156   Canadian Directorate to Casualty Reports
This file contains an extensive code list, presumably to the following Casualty Reports. It is, however, neither in good order nor well preserved.

A.16 2157–2166   Casualty Reports . . .
This file consists of forms containing information on casualties or suspected casualties. Most of the sheets are copies of AGO Form No. 0645 (May 28, 1943) sent to the Machine Records Branch. (The information differs little from that found in the computer punch cards described on page 7.) The entries are arranged as indicated by large geographic areas and thereunder alphabetically by surname. The Casualty Reports from the "Philippine Islands Area" are not well preserved.

2157   Casualty Reports: Germany ILAG (A to Corr)

2158   Casualty Reports: Germany ILAG (Cors to Gol)

2159   Casualty Reports: Germany ILAG (Gons to Kinc)

2160   Casualty Reports: Germany ILAG (King to Mit)

2160A   Casualty Reports: Germany ILAG (Miz to O)

2161   Casualty Reports: Germany ILAG (Pa to Sh)

Box	Contents

2162   Casualty Reports: Germany ILAG (Si to Welc)

2162A   Casualty Reports: Germany ILAG (Weld to Z)

2163   Casualty Reports: Japan A to H

2164   Casualty Reports: Japan I to Z

2165–2166   Casualty Reports: Philippine Islands Area

A.17   2167   Cavender, Charles C. Col. to Civilians, Repatriated
Contains 2 inches of censorship files that list and offer comment on sections removed from the correspondence of American and Axis POWs and their correspondents. There is also a file of civilian wartime internees arranged by location and thereunder generally alphabetically by surname.

A.18   2168–2170   Civilian Returning from France to Foreign Missions (A-T)
The "Missions" files are arranged roughly alphabetically by the name of the denomination or religious order. There is also a file on War Department civilian employees captured by the Japanese in the Pacific early in the war (notably on Wake Island and Guam).

A.19   2171–2175A   Death Lists . . .
These lists are in file folders arranged alphabetically by category or geographic location.

2171   Conarky, French Guinea to Davao Penal Colony

2172   Death Lists: Germany #1–#37

2173   Death Lists: Germany #38–#76 to Transport Carrying T.U.'s

2174   Death Lists: Germany #77–#80

2175–2175A   Death Reports and Lists: (Europe and Asia) Baguio to Zentsuji

A.20   2176–2178   Diaries: Anderson, P.M. to Wood, J.L.
These files consist of responses by former POWs and others to POW Information Bureau inquiries, mostly in 1946, if they had retained diaries or journals of their wartime experiences that they were willing to share. The "diaries" vary in size and level of detail. Some are short letters, while others are long formal reports, a few of which contain day-by-day accounts of internment. They are arranged in alphabetical order by the surname of the respondent. The vast

majority were written by former POWs, but a few were the work of civilians or others, such as military personnel who participated in the liberation of POW camps or the repatriation of POWs. The following list contains an indication of the rank or status of the writer when known, as well as a few notes on the longer "diaries."

Box	**Contents**

Genovese, John A.
Gillespie, James O. (Cpl.)
Goldblith, Samuel A. (Capt.)
Green, John Plath
Guggenheim, R.E. (Capt.)
Hamlin, Harold S. (Lt. Comdr.)
Hancock, Frank
Hawes, Milton D. (Capt.)
Hill, Max
Hochman, David (1st Lt.)
Junod, Marcel, Dr.
Howard, S.L. (Col., USMC)
Hucks, Jessie J. (M. Sgt.)
Jacobs, Eugene
Kentner, ? ("Kentner's Journal")
Keen, Campbell (Capt., USN)
Lingo, Edward F. (Capt.)
Loman, K.E. (Capt.)
MacMillan, George (Capt., USN)
Maher, A.L. (Capt., USN)
Mayger, William
McGee, John H. (Col.)
Moore, George M. (Capt.)
Morris, George E., Jr. (Lt. Comdr.)
Norwood, James L.
O'Gara, Francis Joseph
Oliver, Alfred C., Jr. (Col.)
Olson, John E. (Maj.)
Pappas, William
Pase, Joseph G.
Peart, Cecil J. (Pharmacist's Mate, USN)
   A journal of about 60 pages.
Perfili, Antonio (Cpl.)
Reiner, R.O.

2178   Rogers, Winthrop H. (Maj.)
Samson, Walter E.
Sartin, L.B. (Capt., Medical Corps, USN)
Saunders, M.D.S. (Lt. Col.)
Sharp, Clifton L.
Shearer, ? ("Shearer's Journal")
   Filed with "Sartin, L.B." as one of the reports on medical problems
   and care in Japanese-controlled camps. Together the two reports
   equal about 130 pages.
Shellhorn, Melvin W. (Sgt.)

Box	Contents

Shreve, Arthur L. (Lt. Col.)
Simon, Victor
Stoddard, Ira Ellis
Stubbs, G.H. (Col.)
Thyson, Leo Cromwell (Capt.)
Van Peenen, H.J. (Lt. Comdr., USMC)
Wainwright, J.M. (Gen.)
Ward, John L.
Weible, Charley D.
Wells, Arthur
Wilson, Henry Stanley (Maj.)
Wilterdink, W.H. (Capt., USN)
Wood, John L.

A.21 2179   Donations to International Red Cross to Employees–naval Air Base,
Guam and Manila
    Contains a short report on the fates of the captured "Doolittle
    Raiders" and the "Donovan Report" on camp conditions in Macas-
    sar, Celebes, and Java.

A.22 2180   Escapee Reports
    Mostly lists, arranged by the location of the escape, with a little cor-
    respondence.

A.23 2181-2185   Eto Letters: August 1943–October 1945 to ETO Letter Control

A.24 2186–2186A   ETO Letters #56 to #99
    Consists of status reports on POWs in Europe.

A.25 2187   Evacuees to Foreign and Imperial Censorship Reports

A.26 2188   Former POW List
    The list is for U.S. Navy personnel, Dec. 7, 1941–Dec. 31, 1946,
    compiled ca. 1950.

2188A   Forms (Japanese)
    The forms are completed cards listing American POWs in Japanese
    hands, arranged in alphabetical order by surname.

A.27 2189   Germany: Roster of American and Other Allied Civilian Internees,
A to Z
    Includes an updated alphabetical listing for Japan.

A.28 2190   German-American POWs and Internees

Box	Contents

Gap in Box Numbering

A.29 2197 German-American POWs
Contains the report "American PsOW [sic] in Germany, Nov. 1, 1945" (MID); additional lists of American POWs in German hands; and postwar reports on conditions in German camps and in Japanese camps located outside of Japan.

2197A Germany (and Japan): POWs Miscellaneous

A.30 2198 Germany: Health to Reviews (Miscellaneous)
Contains a file on POWs on Guam.

Gap in Box Numbering

A.31 2201 Internees: List of American Civilians Interned by Japan: Borneo to Philippine Islands Internment Camp

A.32 2202 Internees: List of American Civilians Interned by Japan: Santo Tomas to Tagbilaran

A.33 2203 Internees: Lists of American Civilians Formerly Detained by the German and the Japanese Government

Gap in Box Numbering

A.34 2205–2206 Interrogation (G-2) Report: 26-280
Arranged in numerical order.

2206A Interrogation Reports (Accompanying Letters) to Italy

A.35 2207–2208 Japan: American POW Lists
Box 2208 contains a list of POW camp codes and abbreviations for German- and Japanese-controlled camps.

A.36 2209–2212 Japan: American POW Lists: Batavia Hospital–Zentsuji Camp
Arranged alphabetically by camp name or location.

Gap in Box Numbering

A.37 2216 Java: Miscellaneous to Liberation, Evacuation, And Care of Pow and Civilian Internees in Japan

A.38 2217 Lists: Far East Civilians to Korea and Manchukuo (Manchurian) POWs
Includes Germany, Japan, and a list of French Army casualties in

Box	Contents

North Africa. One of the German lists includes dates and places of birth for American POWs.

A.39 2218   Lists: Merchant Marines (Identified) to Philippine Scouts
Includes a roster of officers and soldiers at OFLAG 64 June 6, 1943–Jan. 11, 1945, omitting quarantined officers.

A.40 2219   Lists: Rabaul, New Britain to Recovered Personnel
The "Recovered Personnel" file is for various countries.

A.41 2220   Lists: Recovered Civilians, Los Banos P.I. to Rennes Hospital

A.42 2221   Lists: Repatriates from Far East to Returned to Military Control
The "Returned to Military Control" (RMC) file is arranged chronologically by date of return.

A.43 2222   Lists: Returned to Military Control to Usaffe Allied Civilians

A.44 2223–2223A   Lists: USMC in the Far East to Memos
Contains several code sheets for the codes that were used on the IBM punch cards, including casualty area codes and codes for both German and Japanese camps.

A.45 2224–2232   Messages . . .
These files consist of messages sent between both American and Axis POWs and their families and loved ones and of correspondence related to those messages. Arrangement is according to a scheme devised to administer the exchange and is not conducive to locating messages by individuals or locations.

    2224   Messages: SA 1 to USO 150

    2225   Messages: USO 151 to USO 500

    2226-2232   Messages: January 1943–October 1945

A.46 2233   Military Intelligence Reports to NATOUSA POW List

    2233A   Monetary Effects of Deceased USA POWs

A.47 2234   Navy Code to Personal Funds Removed from Deceased American POWs in Japanese Prison Camps
Includes a list of nurses captured in the Pacific.

A.48 2235   Philippine Campaign (First) to Photographs

Box	Contents

Includes lists of American POWs. The photographs (about 20) are prints (some captured) that were apparently selected as representative of both German- and Japanese-controlled camps.

A.49 2236-2238   Postal Censor List #1-529

A.50 2239   POW Camps (Germany) to POW Strength Reports

A.51 2240   POW Reports: April to Oct. 1944

A.52 2241   POW Reports Nov. 1944 to Puerto Princesa (Camp 10a)
The foregoing "reports" are lists.

     2241A   POWs Added to List According to Captured Personnel Records

A.53 2242   PWCL #1-400 to Questionnaire (MIS-X)
The PWCL are lists of POWs that give at least name, next of kin, and address, and sometimes more information, such as name of camp and date of capture. The questionnaires are the MIS-X questionnaires that were applied by intelligence units concerning POW treatment and experiences in the India-Burma theater.

A.54 2243   Receipts for Salary to Recovered Personnel, L
Contains reports and correspondence on such subjects as liberation of POW camps and messages to and from POWs.

     2243A   Receipts for Salary

A.55 2244   Recovered Personnel, L to Recovery Team #5
Information on recovered personnel concerns those held in Japanese-controlled POW camps. The recovery team reports are reports and correspondence from teams assigned to liberate POW camps.

A.56 2245   Recovery Team #7 to Relief of American Lists of Internees in the Philippines

A.57 2246   Repatriates from Belgium to Repatriates, Ship Lists

A.58 2247   Repatriates, Ship Lists from Rumania to Repatriated on RMC
The two boxes of files on repatriation are arranged alphabetically by geographic indicator—city, country, or general region. For instance "Far East" precedes "Germany," which precedes "Goteberg."

A59 2248   Reports: British-ARC to Rules and Regulations for POWs

Box	**Contents**

A.60 2249–2254 RMC [Returned to Military Control] Lists . . .
There are 8 volumes for German-controlled camps and 2 volumes for Japanese-controlled camps. Within each volume, the entries are in alphabetical order by surname. The lists generally contain name, serial number, grade, service branch, dates held, and place of detention.

2249 RMC Lists: Germany September 1944–May 16, 1945

2250 RMC Lists: Germany May 1–30, 1945

2251 RMC Lists: Germany May 31–June 8, 1945

2252 RMC Lists: Germany June 9–20, 1945

2253 RMC Lists: Germany June 20–27, 1945

2254 RMC Lists: Germany June 27, 1945 to RMC Lists, Japan

A.61 2255 Rosters Barth Luft I, STG I RUS 11998

2255A–2259 RUS 11894 to 12569

A.62 2260 RUSC 1867 to RUSCJA 2148
Contains lists of POWs who died in Germany and the Philippines.

A.63 2261 SEATIC Intelligence Bulletin #25 and #29 to Signal Corps: SC 455(1)
Consists partly of intelligence reports of the Southeast Asia Translation Interrogation Center concerning treatment of POWs and conditions in camps in the area.

A.64 2262–2274 Signal Corps [Messages/Cables]

2262–66 Signal Corps WA 1(5)–WA 1313

2267–74 Signal Corps WB 1314–YE 562

A.65 2275–2275A Signal Corps [Messages/cables] Without Numbers to Wehsien CACRMC Report

A.66 2276 Sinkings
Contains lists of POWs, narratives, reports, and correspondence concerning the sinkings of Japanese transports carrying American prisoners.

Box		Contents

A.67 2277   State Dept. to Status of American POW
The former relates to Americans in the Far East; the latter to
POWs in German hands.

A.68 2278–2279   Steamships . . .
Contains reports, lists, and correspondence concerning wartime sail-
ings of ships of various nations. The records concern both American and "enemy alien" passengers.

2278   Steamships: *Admiral Williams* to *Gripsholm*

2279   Steamships: *Gripsholm* to SS *William F. Humphrey*

A.69 2280   Summaries of International Committee of Red Cross to Treatment of
POWs Japan

A.70 2281   Unidentified U.S. POWs List to YMCA (POWs in Germany)

Appendix B

Index to Files on Japanese-Controlled POW Camps (World War II)
from general subject file, 1942–46
American POW Information Bureau, Records Branch
Records of the Office of the Provost Marshal General, 1941–
Record Group 389

B.1   This index was produced because the records it covers are particularly rich in "first person accounts" by Americans who were in Japanese-controlled POW camps in World War II. Also, the Japanese camps, unlike the German, were not named, nor indeed administered, in a particularly orderly fashion. Therefore, access to the files regarding the records on Japanese-held POWs is more difficult than it is for records of German-held POWs. See the text, **II.5–II.10**, and Appendix A, **A.12**, for a further description of the records.

B.2   The apparent irregularity in camp names, as well as the alternative spellings of a handful of East Asian languages, creates difficulties in indexing. Because of that, most main entries are reproduced verbatim from the folder titles in the records. Departure from this convention occurs only in the case of obvious errors, such as "Yokohoma" for Yokohama. Cross-references and secondary entries have been used generously and, it is hoped, with some imagination. **Those entries that are exact folder titles are printed in boldface.**

B.3   The entries, except for a few cross-references, are keyed to the numbers of the boxes in which the records are now housed. It must be remembered that the processes of records preservation and holdings maintenance sometimes dictate that records be reboxed. Should reboxing occur, every effort will be made to minimize and document any changes in this finding aid. Indeed, preservation work on the series was performed after this index was constructed. The only change was to add boxes at positions in the file where boxes were originally too full. Those new boxes are few and each is numbered like the preceding box with the addition of the suffix "A." Thus the researcher should be aware that in these few cases a request for a box listed in this index (such as 2126) will produce two boxes (2126 and 2126A) and that the record sought might be in either box.

B.4   The index is arranged into three large geographic headings:

China, Korea, and Manchuria

Japan

Southeast Asia and the Pacific Islands

Thereunder, the entries are arranged alphabetically, except for camps or other installations with numeric designations, which are arranged numerically before the alphabetic entries.

In some cases, especially for camps within Japan, names consist of numerical or numero-alphabetic designations attached to the name of a specific site and/or geographic area. Some examples are "Fukuoka #1 (Kashi)"; "Hakodate Branch Camp 3"; and "Niigata 5-B, Tokyo 5-B (Daigo Bunsho)." These camp names are entered under the most easily recognized geographic heading and thereunder in numeric or numero-alphabetic order. They are liberally covered by secondary and cross-references. No effort was made to conventionalize the numeric and numero-alphabetic camp names. They are given here as found in the records. Thus their format varies, both in its order and in the use of symbols such as "#" and "-", and abbreviations such as "No." Remember that the names used are those found in the folder titles of the files produced by the Prisoner of War Information Bureau, and are not necessarily exactly those given to the camps by the Japanese.

B.5 Material in the index that is enclosed in brackets has been added by the editor and is of three types:

1. information offered as clarification to an entry, such as the expansion of an incomplete place name ("Tanjong Pagar [Singapore]") or the term necessary to connect a secondary reference to a main entry ("Funatsu [Nagoya #3-B]");

2. indications of cases in which there are two or more file folders with the same title in the same box, such as "[2]"; and

3. information about the records themselves that could be of interest to the researcher, such as "[empty file]," "[map]," and "[photographs]."

CHINA, KOREA, AND MANCHURIA

	Box
Bowen Road Military Hospital, Hong Kong, China	2121
Bridge House Jail, Shanghai, China	2121
Canton, China	2121
Fengtai, China	2121
FORMOSA. *See* "SOUTHEAST ASIA AND THE PACIFIC ISLANDS, FORMOSA"	
Glenro Camp (?)	2121
HONG KONG	
Bowen Road Military Hospital	2121
Hong Kong [2]	2121
Shamshuipo POW Camp	2121
Stanley Camp	2121
Hoten Camp, Mukden, Manchuria	2134
Hoten Main Camp, Mukden, Manchuria	2134

	Box
18 Kilo, Burma-Thailand Railroad	2120
80 Kilo, Burma-Thailand Railroad	2120
100 Kilo, Burma-Thailand Railroad	2120
142d General Hospital	2120
Bangkok, Thailand [2]	2120
Bataan [Philippines]	2135
Batavia, Java [empty file]	2120
Bilibid POW Camp, P.I.	2135
Brenkassey, Thailand	2120
BURMA	
general [2]	2120
Moulmein	2120
New Law Courts, Rangoon	2120
Rangoon	2120
Rangoon Jail	2120
Burma-Thailand Railroad [map]	2120
BURMA-THAILAND RAILROAD CAMPS	
18 Kilo	2120
80 Kilo	2120
100 Kilo	2120
Burma-Thailand Railroad [map]	2120
Tah Makam (Tamarkan)	2120
Tamarkan (Tah Makam)	2120
Thanbyuzayat	2120
Cabanatuan POW Camp #1, P.I. [3]	2135
Camp No. 7, Corregidor, Philippine Military Prison	2135
Camp O'Donnell (Philippines) [2]	2135
Cebu No. 30 [Philippines]	2135
Changi, Singapore	2134
Changi Barracks (Singapore)	2134
Changi POW Camp, Singapore	2134
Changi-Singapore Island-Malay states [empty file]	2134
Corregidor [Camp No. 7, Philippine Military Prison]	2135
Dalat, Indo-China	2123
Davao Penal Colony [Philippines]	2135
Erangi (Hospital) Singapore Island	2134
FORMOSA	
Heito [Taiwan #3]	2122
Karenko Camp, Taiwan	2122

Appendix C

FOLDER LIST FOR THE SERIES
NAVY PRISONER OF WAR BOARD SUBJECT FILES, 1942–45
RECORDS OF THE CASUALTY SECTION;
RECORD GROUP 24—RECORDS OF THE BUREAU OF NAVAL PERSONNEL

C.1   See **II.19** for additional information on this series and its context regarding other records.

FILE DESIGNATION	SUBJECT

C.2   A   Establishment and duties of POW Board, agreements between Navy Department and Red Cross

C.3   B   General
         B-I   Army jurisdiction over POWs; Army/Navy agreement

C.4   C   Minutes of meetings

OFFICIAL LISTS OF AMERICAN PRISONERS OF WAR

C.5   Many of the records in the following folders are copies of information from the POW Information Bureau of the Army's Office of the Provost Marshal General. Names are included, and are often accompanied by service number, "POW number," and unit, and sometimes by home address and name of next of kin. There are occasionally postal censorship lists that contain stateside addresses and names of correspondents. The records are arranged as listed, but under like headings the Roman numeral breakdowns are for lists that were transferred from the POW Information Bureau during certain time periods. Thereunder, the records are sometimes arranged alphabetically by surname, and sometimes unarranged.

FILE DESIGNATION	SUBJECT

C.6   D   Navy, Marine Corps, Coast Guard

C.7   E-I   Army - Far East - Japan
        E-II   Army - Far East - Japan

C.8   F-I   Army - Europe - Germany
        F-II   Army - Europe - Germany
        F-III   Army - Europe - Germany

FILE DESIGNATION	SUBJECT
F-IV	Army - Europe - Germany
F-V	Army - Europe - Germany
F-VI	Army - Europe - Germany
F-VII	Army - Europe - Germany
F-VIII	Army - Europe - Germany
F-IX	Army - Europe - Germany
F-X	Army - Europe - Germany
F-XI	Army - Europe - Germany
F-XII	Army - Europe - Germany

C.9   G   Army - Europe and Africa - Italians

OFFICIAL LIST OF AMERICAN CIVIL INTERNEES

C.10   H-I   Far East
          H-II   Europe

C.11   I   [Press] releases

LISTS OF MISSING AND CHANGES OF STATUS

C.12   J-I   Navy, Naval Reserve, Coast Guard
          J-II   Marine Corps
          J-II(a)   Marine Corps

UNOFFICIAL LIST AND PROBABLY POWS

C.13   J   [untitled]
          K-I   Prisoners of War and Civilian Internees
          K-II   List of Probably Prisoners of War [empty file]

CUSTODY AND TRANSFER

C.14   L-I   Custody interrogation, work and transfer of POW
          L-Ia   War Department regulations governing POWs
          L-Ib   Personal punishment and military discipline—S.W. Pacific area
          L-Ic   Regulations concerning employment of POWs—S.W. Pacific area
          L-Id   Procedure in interrogating and handling POWs
          L-II   Transfer between Allies

C.15 The records in this section consist largely of copies of U.S. State Department and International Red Cross correspondence, and an occasional intelligence report from MID. Many of the files are arranged by camp name.

File Designation	Subject
C.16 M-I	Japanese homeland
M-IA	Japanese homeland
M-Ia	POW camps—Japan and Japanese occupied territories
M-Ib	POW camp conditions—Japan
M-Ic	Monthly summary on location and composition of POW camps in Japanese occupied territory
M-II	Shanghai area
M-III	Philippines
M-IIIa	POWs in the Philippine Islands
M-IV	Occupied territory except foregoing
M-IVa	POW camp conditions on the Asiatic mainland
M-IVb	POW camps in Taiwan (Formosa)
M-IVc	Location and strengths of POW camps and civil assembly centers in Japan and Japanese occupied territory
M-IVd	Location and composition of POW camps in Japanese occupied territory
M-IVe	Location and composition of POW camps in Japanese occupied territory
C.17 N-I	Germany and Satellites
N-II	Germany and Satellites
N-III	Germany and Satellites
N-IV	Germany and Satellites
N-V	Germany and Satellites
N-VI	Germany and Satellites
C.18 EO	Italy
C.19 P	American and Allied

Relief

C.20 Many records in the following folders are copies of U.S. State Department and International Red Cross correspondence. The Red Cross bulletins in "Q-III" appear to be a complete set of those published during the war.

FILE	
DESIGNATION	**SUBJECT**
X-II	Repatriation—sick and wounded POWs—Germany
X-IIa	Exchange of government officials, protected personnel, merchant seamen, and civilian nation[al]s—Germany

MISCELLANEOUS

C.29	Y	Captured enemy documents and enemy broadcasts
C.30	Z	Escapes and attempted escapes of POWs and internees
	Z-I	Japan and Japanese-occupied territories
	Z-II	Germany and satellites
	Z-III	Shanghai area

Index

This index covers the text of the reference information paper and Appendixes A and C (Appendix B is itself an index). All index entries that begin with a Roman numeral (e.g. **IV.12**) refer to paragraphs in the body of the reference information paper. An index entry that begins with the letters A or C (e.g. **A.14**) refers to a numbered entry in the respective appendix.

POW camps are treated here under the heading "camps, POW," followed by subject headings.

Geographic names generally refer to POW camp locations and are separate entries, except for "Japan" and "Germany," which are mentioned too often to be indexed. However, there are entries such as "Germany (POW camps in)" and "Japan (POW camps in)" when the records contain systematic lists of such camps or collections of reports on them. Entries for record groups refer to the first paragraph after the record group heading in the text.

atomic bomb - III.21.12
Austria - III.12.4
awards - V.4, V.5

Baden-Baden - II.32.2
Baguio, Philippine Islands - A.19
Barcelona - I.5.4
Bari, Italy - V.12.11
Bataan - III.18, III.20, V.12.10, V.12.12, V.12.13, V.16.32, V.19.3
Batavia Hospital - A.36
Beebe, Brigadier General Lewis C. - V.16.31
Belfort Gap Region - V.9.1
Bermuda - II.21
Bern, Switzerland - A.8
Bilibid, Philippine Islands - IV.3, V.12.9, V.19.6
Borneo - A.31
Bowler, Colonel Louis J. - V.16.31
British Ministry of Information - V.12.5
Bucharest - V.12.11
Buchenwald - III.12.2
Bulgaria - A.14
Burma - A.12

Cabanatuan Prison Camp, Philippine Islands - V.12.9, V.12.13, V.19.5, V.29, A.9
cables - II.4, II.6
Caen, Normandy - V.16.27
camps
    concentration - III.12.2, V.18.2
    POW - II.19, II.32.3–II.32.5, V.10-V.11
        activities in - V.16.31
        administration of - III.21
        Allied - C.19
        American - C.19
        Camp Holmes, Philippine Islands - II.31
        Camp O'Donnell, Luzon - III.21.12
        conditions in - II.9.7, II.9.19, II.27, III.12.1, III.12.4, III.18, III.21.2, III.21.5, V.30, A.29, A.63, C.15–C.19
        histories of - II.8, III.21.4
        Japanese-controlled. *See* Appendix B.
        maps and sketches - II.9.21, II.23–II.24
        names - C.16–C.19
        religious affairs - III.9.16, V.17.2
        reports on - II.5, II.28.2-II.28.3, III.21.11, A.1, A.14, A.29, C.15–C.19
        rosters from - A.61
Canadian Directorate - A.15
captured enemy records - V.8.1, V.9.1, V.15-V.17.3, V.19.1, V.19.5, V.19.7, A.52, C.29
Cassino, Italy - V.16.28

casualties - II.28.7, III.6, IV.2, A.15–A.16, A.19

Cavender, Colonel Charles C. - A.17

Celebes - A.21

censorship - A.11, A.17, A.25, A.49, C.5, C.22

chaplains - III.32–III.35

Chaplains, Records of the Office of Chief of (RG 247) - III.32

China - A.14

civilian internees -.I.1, I.5.1, I.7.3, II.4.4, II.9.5, II.13.1, II.13.10, II.19, II.20, II.21, II.28.1, II.29, II.32, II.33, III.1–III.2, III.12.4, III.12.6, III.18, III.19, III.21.10, III.22.1, III.22.4, III.22.5, III.22.8, III.22.9, III.22.10, III.28, III.32, III.35, IV.14.1, V.28, V.36, A.9, A.17, A.18, A.20, A.27, A.32, A.33, A.37, A.38, A.41, A.43, A.56, C.10–C.11, C.22, C.25, C.28

    capture of - II.32.4

    diaries of - A.20

    liberation of - V.14.1

    next of kin of - II.32.2, II.32.4, II.32.5

    occupations of - II.32.4

    race of - III.12.4

claims, financial - II.20

clergy - II.31, III.32–III.35

Coast Guard personnel, U.S. - I.5.1, III.17, C.6, C.12

Combined Chiefs of Staff (CCS) - II.22

Conarky, French Guinea - A.19

Corregidor - V.12.10, V.12.13, V.16.31, V.16.32, V.19.2, V.19.3, V.19.5

courts martial, Japanese Army - III.17

Croatia - A.14

Cuimba [Guimba?] East Central School - V.11

Czechoslovakia - A.14

Davao, Philippine Islands - II.31.5, A.19

deaths in combat - V.5

decimal classification scheme, War Department - III.12.6, III.35

decimal file, State Department - II.33

Denmark - A.14

dependents of U.S. citizens - II.4.5, II.20

diplomacy - II.3, A.10–A.11

displaced persons - II.29

donated materials - V.19, V.31

Doolittle Raid - A.21, C.27

Drottningholm, SS - II.32.1

Eisenhower, General Dwight David - V.18.2

enemy aliens - A.68

European Theater of Operations - II.28, III.29, IV.4.2, V.12.8, A.6, A.24

Evacuation Hospital, 92d (Philippine Islands) - V.11

Featherstone Riot - C.27

motion pictures - V.6-V.19

Mukden, Manchuria, POW camp - V.19.9

Nagasaki - III.21.12

naturalized U.S. citizens - II.4.5

Naval Operations, Records of the Office of Chief of (RG 38) - IV.3

Naval Personnel, Records of the Bureau of (RG 24) - II.17, IV.2, Appendix C

Naval Reserve personnel, U.S. - IV.5.2

Navy, 1789–1947, General Records of the Department of the (RG 80) - V.25

Navy personnel - II.17–II.19, IV.5.2, V.5.1, V.25–V.26, A.26, C.3, C.6, C.12

Navy Prisoner of War Board - Appendix C

neutral countries - II.4.3, II.28.5

New Britain - A.40

newsreels - V.6, V.19

   German - V.19.1

Niigata Camp - V.31

Nissen No. 2 (Japanese POW camp) - V.19.8

Nuernberg - III.13-III.14

Nuernberg, U.S. Military Tribunals - III.10, III.13

nurses - II.17, III.5, V.12.4, V.12.10, V.16.31, A.47

occupation of Japan - III.1, III.7–III.9

occupation of the Philippines by the Japanese - V.16.31

Office of Strategic Services - V.12.16

Office of War Information, Records of the (RG 208) - V.14

Omori POW camp - V.19.8, V.31

Palawan Camp, Philippine Islands - V.29

Palmyra Island, civilian workers on - II.21

paratroopers, U.S. Army - V.16.12

Paris - V.9.2, V.16.6, V.16.20, V.19.7

personal accounts - III.21.4

personnel files - III.8

petitions - III.6

Philippine Archives Collection - III.19-III.22

Philippine Islands - I.5.1, II.4.4, II.27, II.31, II.32.2, III.19–III.22, IV.3, V.7, V.8.2, V.10, V.12.7, V.12.12, V.12.13, V.16.31, V.17.1, V.28.6, V.28.7, V.29, A.9, A.14, A.16, A.19, A.20, A.31–A.32, A.48, A.62, C.16, Appendix B

   civilian workers in - II.20, II.21

Philippine Scouts - A.39

POW Information Bureau - II.4, II.28, A.1, C.5, Appendix B

POWs

   Allied - II.23, III.14, V.9.2, V.16.11, V.16.14, V.16.17, V.16.23, V.16.31, V.30, C.27

   Axis - II.23, II.27, II.29, II.30, II.32, V.28, A.17, A.45, C.26

   birth data of - II.26

   British - V.9.2, V.16.11, V.16.23

   capture of - II.15.10, II.19, II.26, II.27

prisons - II.23

propaganda - III.2, C.29

propaganda (Japanese) about POW camps - V.30

property settlements - II.29

protected personnel - I.5.4, C.23

Provost Marshal General, 1941– , Records of the Office of the (RG 389) - II.2, A.1, C.2

Puerto Princesa (Camp 10A) - A.52

Quartermaster General, Records of the Office of the (RG 92) - III.23

Rabaul, New Britain - A.48

Radio Berlin - V.23

Radio Tokyo - V.23

Rangers, U.S. - V.12.8

recovered personnel - A.40, A.55

Red Cross. *See* International Red Cross or American National Red Cross

Red Cross Bulletins - C.20

refugees - II.29

relatives of military personnel - IV.5

relief - C.20–C.21

religious orders - A.18

relocation centers - II.31

repatriation - II.32–II.32.5, III.5, A.17

returned to military control (RMC) - II.4.3, II.13.7, II.13.10, II.27.7, II.28.7, A.6, A.42–A.43, A.60

Roman Catholics - II.4.4

Rome - V.13

Rumania - A.14, A.58

San Francisco, California - II.32.4, V.19.5

Santo Tomas, Philippine Islands - II.31.1, II.31.2, V.7, A.32

Saturday Evening Post - A.20

Sendai Camp - V.31

Shanghai - I.5.1, II.20, C.16, C.30

ship lists - A.57, A.68

Siam - A.12, A.14

Signal Corps (Army) - V.12, V.27, V.31, A.63, A.63–A.65

Signal Officer, Records of the Office of the Chief (RG 111) - V.12, V.27

sinkings. *See* transport ships

slave labor - III.12.1, III.12.3

sound recordings - V.20–V.24

Southeast Asia Translation Interrogation Center (SEATIC) - A.63

Special War Problems Division (Department of State) - II.29, II.32, A.14

St. Raphael - V.12.2

State, General Records of the Department of (RG 59) - II.29

State Department, U.S. - A.14, A.67, C.15, C.20, C.24

still pictures - V.25–V.31